My Rocky Mountain Challenge

Adventures of a Misfit

Daniel J. Millette

Copyright © MMXXIII
Saskatchewan, Canada
Launch Publishing

My Rocky Mountain Challenge

Adventures of a Misfit

Editing by Shavonne Clarke
Cover art by Duy Phan

ISBN eBook: 978-1-7780525-8-3
ISBN Paperback: 978-1-7780525-7-6

danieljmillette.substack.com
www.youtube.com/@DanielJMillette
www.facebook.com/DanielJMillette

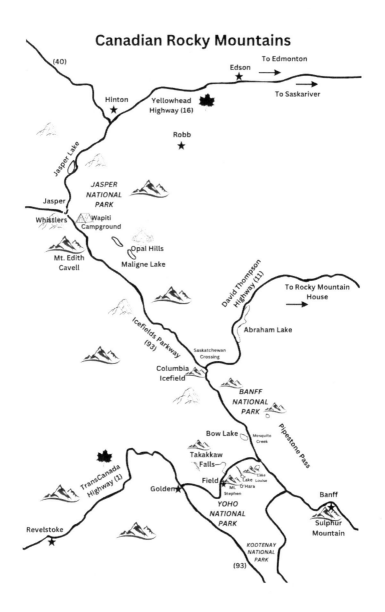

Canadian Rocky Mountains

(40)

To Edmonton

Edson ★

To Saskariver

Hinton ★

Yellowhead
Highway (16)

Robb ★

Jasper Lake

JASPER
NATIONAL
PARK

Jasper

Whistlers

Wapiti
Campground

Mt. Edith
Cavell

Opal Hills

Maligne Lake

David Thompson
Highway (11)

To Rocky Mountain
House

Abraham Lake

Icefields Parkway
(93)

Saskatchewan
Crossing

Columbia
Icefield

BANFF
NATIONAL
PARK

Bow Lake

Mosquito
Creek

Pipestone Pass

Takakkaw
Falls

TransCanada
Highway (1)

Golden ★

Field

Lake
Louise

Lake
O'Hara

Mt.
Stephen

Banff ★

Sulphur
Mountain

YOHO
NATIONAL
PARK

Revelstoke ★

KOOTENAY
NATIONAL
PARK

(93)

DISCLAIMER

*T*his book is a work of fiction. Characters are fictional. Events are fictional. Evil National Park employees are fictional. IS THIS CLEAR? The author does not have time for petty fictional assertions claiming otherwise.

DEDICATION

To my wonderful children.
Thanks for all the crazy mountain adventures.
Here's to many more.

A Thought

"I am an ignorant pilgrim, crossing a dark valley. And yet for a long time, looking back, I have been unable to shake off the feeling that I have been led—make of that what you will."

——Wendell Berry, *Jayber Crow*

CHAPTER ONE

CATASTROPHE

I'm in jail.

Eleven years old, no less. I'll probably never make anything of my life now. Bounce from prison to prison. See the sights and sounds of what different lockups have to offer. Lift weights all day. Get a nickname like *Bones* or *Skullface*. Work on a life skill that I'll never use. Maybe eventually get a job with the government—the usual criminal stuff.

At least I won't be lonely. I'll have my family with me. Yep, they're in jail with me. And there are a lot of us. There's my dad, Marc (41), and my mom, Geri (she says I'm not supposed to tell others her age). Then there are my siblings: Johnny (17), Josh (14), Ellie (13), Rebecca (6), Sam (4), and the baby, Lyda. We're all criminals. The worst thing is that our Rocky Mountain trip is wasting away. We're in a cell in Banff, Alberta. If I could see through these brick walls, I'd see the inspiring Cascade Mountain, the crisp and clear Bow River, and maybe an annoyed elk posing for picture-obsessed tourists. But I can't see through walls.

I'm hungry. Will they feed us? It's been...minutes since I last ate. Getting weak...

And now my little sister is crying. She's wailing. Even the prison guard moved to another room. Will someone get me out of this prison?

I'm ahead of myself once again. I guess I've got time to tell the story. Sit back. Relax. Get your tissues out. My sob story is at hand. You'll feel sorry for me when I'm finished. I hope.

I'd better backtrack a few weeks.

"Joey! Stop trying to feed Lyda cat food!"

"Joey, did you burn the garbage yet? You've already lost two years of allowance just from this past month."

"Joey, why are my Barbie dolls on the roof?"

"Joey, I'm going to feed you to my tarantula!"

"Joey! You're TOO MUCH!"

Yes, I'm Joey. Joey Storthoaks. We live on an acreage near the small town of Saskariver, Saskatchewan, where the vast prairie meets the northern forest. We love the outdoors, having fun, and causing trouble. We're a large family. Some people make fun of us for that. Some people are dumb.

As you can see, I've been a bit of trouble lately. *A lot* of trouble, actually. I don't know why. I got in trouble once. Then I got in trouble again. Next thing you know, I was an—what did Mom say?—attention-grabbing juvenile delinquent just like my father. Some say it's because I'm homeschooled while my older siblings attend "real" school. That's not true. I love homeschooling. I'm just...finding myself in this world. Expressing myself. Becoming my own individual. Right?

I don't fit in so well. But that's usually by choice. I'm a misfit of sorts. But who isn't?

"Joey! Darn it! Did you eat all the chips? They were for our trip!"

"Joey! Why's my toothbrush in the toilet?"

This latest round of blowups was all about timing, really. We were preparing for a family vacation. By *vacation* I mean trip, because taking seven kids camping isn't a vacation, as my mom always says. I was being a brat because I was excited, okay? It was just a bit inconvenient for everyone else.

This year, we were going to the Rocky Mountains. I'd never been there. My parents had been many years ago. They would tell us stories of people feeding bears, climbing mountains like a walk in the park, and water being so clear you could drop a coin in and still read the date on the coin thirty feet down. I think either they've been exaggerating, or things have changed. I was about to find out.

"Geri, did all the kids pack their bags?" asked Dad.

"Just need another stack of a hundred diapers, and we should be good," said Mom.

"Good news! I found our tent. It'll run away on you when you don't use it in over twenty years."

"What shape is it in?"

"Tent-shaped."

The excitement was building. Our own mountain adventure! I thought only rich people with fifty-foot campers and no kids went on mountain adventures! Were we ready for the mountains? Were the mountains ready for us?

"Joey, our neighbor George is here. Show him how to feed the animals and stuff. He's going to check in every day while we're away." As she said this, my mom was busy making a five-foot stack of sandwiches for the road.

I heard before George was what you'd call well-read. As if you could read books and become smart, just like that. I took George out to our chicken coop. I showed him where we kept the feed, where the eggs were usually laid, which chickens would try to kill him, and how much food to give to our dog named Doggy, horse named Horse, and thirty or so cats named everything from Helmet-Gotchies to Couch-Cushion, from the mother cat Bob to the tomcat Cindy-Lou. Checking to see if our cats are male or female is not a strong suit of ours.

"You sure have a lot of cats," said George, spooking two cats with one step.

"They keep the mice down," I told him as a dozen cats lounged on the grass next to the chicken coop. I'd never actually seen a cat of ours catch a mouse. Probably cause they ate them all.

"Well," said George, "can anyone lend me two eighty-pound rats? I want to rid my house of cats."

"You want two what?" I said.

"Nothing," he said. "It's a poem. Shel Silverstein? No?"

"No."

George waved goodbye and drove off. He was a good guy. A little strange. I hear reading does that to you. I kind of liked the idea of being smart, I must admit.

A minute later he was back. He jumped out of his seat, ran to the rear of his car, opened his trunk, and four cats jumped out.

I started laughing at my prank. Dad saw me laughing. He said he'd give me something to laugh about. Oddly enough, I stopped laughing.

That night, we slept, sort of, and then the morning rush was on. We had to do our last round of packing toothbrushes and counting kids. It was Sunday morning, and everything had to be done early so we could hit up church on our way out.

We made it to church. My dad jumped out of the pew at one point and, without a word, drove home. He came back ten minutes later with my brother Sam in tow. At least I wasn't to blame this time.

I was glad Sam came. First off, he's my little buddy. Second, he's very convenient to have at church.

Father Wally was preaching. Father Wally Zsxyltchovskiwehveltskibetishly, to be precise. He came to Canada from—where was it—England? That or Poland. He's a kind man with a gentle face. I like him. Which makes my Sunday tradition seem even worse.

Every Sunday during the preaching, I would look at Sam. He would grin and nod his head. Then I'd whisper to my mom, "Sam needs to pee. I'm going to take him."

Mom would sigh, but I'd be gone before she could answer.

I'd take Sam out back. We'd wander around for a while. Sometimes, he'd use the washroom. Sometimes.

On this particular Sunday, the sun was shining, the birds singing, the air inside the church stifling. So, we made our way outside, Sam and I.

I walked over to our large vehicle. It was loaded with camping gear and food supplies. Maybe we didn't even have room for Sam? I wondered which sibling I'd want to leave behind. Ellie? Josh?

As I gazed at the tires, picturing wild mountain adventures, I smiled at one of our cats, good ole Peaches-n-Salami. Peaches-n-Salami smiled back at me. I turned to head back inside when a brainwave hit. This cat wasn't supposed to be here. Oh to have two eighty-pound rats.

We have a problem with cats hitching rides. Peaches-n-Salami was one of our worst cats for that. I had to go tell Dad. It was my duty. As his son. As a member of the Storthoaks family. As a Christian. As an esteemed resident of Saskariver.

I didn't go tell Dad.

Things happened. Like unavoidable things. Like things that I had no control over. I mean... You see...

I was walking back to the church to tell Dad when I heard the choir start singing. The choir and I are enemies, at least in my mind. I'm always daydreaming of ways to sabotage their work. I probably shouldn't, but I just do. And here was a perfect chance.

A window was open right behind where the choir was located in the church. I could see the backs of older men and women, they were singing about peace. It was time for me to start a war. I smiled at Sam, ran back to the vehicle, scooped up Peaches-n-Salami, and approached the window. With one heave, I tossed the cat up and into the open window. From outside the window, I heard the result.

"Peeeeeeace is floooowing like a...@#%^!"

Meow! Hiss!

"^#%$!!!!"

The music stopped. I heard screams and shouts. Then I heard weird sounds coming from the organ. Like death was giving birth to a clown. I think Peaches-n-Salami was walking on the organ keys. He walks on our piano at home sometimes.

I heard several chairs crash. Some thumping. A cat screeched. A speaker went thud. The microphone shrilled. More yells and swears, followed by a book crashing through a window. More shouts. I was missing it!

I ran into the church with Sam. I saw a mini-riot. People colliding with others. Pushing and shoving. Fingers pointed in blame. That darn cat saw me and ran over to me. He jumped right into my arms, and I held him. He purred gently. Everyone stopped their madness and stared at me.

The silence was deafening.

"Joey!" shouted my mom.

I was dead.

CHAPTER TWO

ON THE ROAD

You don't want to hear all the details. Dad took the cat home. Picked up another cat in the process. Drove that cat back. Lost a few more precious hairs. Church resumed. And afterward, I was threatened with never receiving allowance again, with doing all the home chores for the rest of eternity, with being shipped out of the country, with being blasted off into outer space, with anything you can think of. You know, the usual.

But I will add one point. Father Wally came over while my parents were ending their barrage of threats. He didn't look rattled at all. He had a book in his hands and a smile on his face.

"Joey. I have something for you."

This rattled me. I expected to be screamed at, not gifted with something. Father Wally handed it over. It was a book called *Rocky Mountain Stories*. I was puzzled.

"Um. I heard you've been a bit, well, a bit much lately," said Father Wally gently. "I used to be like that. Then God hit me over the head with a baseball bat one day, and I changed. Anyway, I found this book at the thrift shop a week ago, so I thought you might like it. For your adventures. It might get your mind focused a bit. Just give me a moment. I want to write something in it."

He paused, lost in thought. Then, a light bulb went off in his mind. More than that, Father Wally seemed lost in a vision. He started writing frantically for thirty seconds and handed it back again. I thanked him. We said goodbye and headed off. We were on the road.

I could handle being threatened and yelled at. This anger was justified. But his kindness shook me. Well played, Father Wally.

"Going on a road trip. Gonna have a party. Gonna eat chips. Going on a road trip."

My siblings and I sang this over and over. Until Dad told us he'd stop the vehicle and leave us wherever we were if we sang it just one more time. Yes, we were on the road.

We drove and drove. Lyda cried and cried. Sam stopped to pee and stopped to pee some more. Traveling with nine people is tough slogging. Sometimes we sang. Sometimes people slept. Sometimes we ate. Or rather, sometimes we didn't eat. Most of the time, there was a bag of chips going around or some garden carrots being crunched. At one point, Mom passed around watermelon slices. She said we had to finish it off. Boy did this increase the stops along the side of the road, if you know what I mean.

I didn't read the book. I get motion sickness. I was anxious to look at the book when we stopped, though. Eight hours later, we did finally stop for the night. We were in Edmonton, Alberta.

Edmonton is not a place to camp. It's a scary place. A big, mean place. I hear cats go missing in Edmonton. Probably from eighty-pound rats. So, my dad, oldest brother Johnny, and I went inside a hotel to see if we could get a room.

"Hi, I need a room. Two queen-sized beds, please."

"How many children?" asked the lady at the counter.

My dad hated this question. He knew what this meant. It meant they would charge us more money for each "extra" child we had. As though cramming in a few extra children would bankrupt this international billion-dollar hotel chain.

He looked at Johnny and me and said out loud, "I see two kids here."

The lady at the counter stared in suspicion. "So, you have two children?"

"Yeah, I have two children. For sure, I have two children."

"Two?"

"I'm looking at two children right now. Am I not?"

"Do you have any more children?"

"I have more children," he answered truthfully, "but they are not *here*. See?"

"Alright," she said, tired of this game, "here's your room key. Checkout is at eleven. To get to your room, go up the elevator and number 316 will be on the left.

Dad returned to the vehicle and said, "You guys know what to do."

It was Operation Big-Family-Sneak-In. We sent Mom and the two youngest kids in first. And we waited. Like Gandalf sending in dwarves to Mr. Baggins' place, if you know about *The Hobbit.*

Five minutes later, more siblings entered, carrying sleeping bags. And we waited.

Five minutes later, Dad, Johnny, and I entered, carrying more sleeping bags.

"Don't make eye contact!" hissed Dad as we walked to the elevator.

I could feel the hotel worker staring us down. Her eyes piercing in anger. I imagined she was calling for security, or the police, or a mob of ninjas to tackle us. I didn't look back.

We made it to the hotel room. By the time the sleeping bags were out, there was no place to walk. Such is life in a large family.

That night, I opened my book. *Rocky Mountain Stories.* The pictures were black and white. The stories were long, but not too long. It looked good. Then I remembered that Father Wally had written something, so I flipped to the front of the book.

Joey. You will be needed by others. Be ready for this. You will be needed.
I pray you grow up.

God Bless always,
Fr. Wally Zsxyltchovskiwehveltskibetishly
(Psalm 12-1)

Psalm 12 didn't make sense when I looked it up in the hotel Bible. It said something about loyal people vanishing. Must be poetry. Like eighty-pound rats chasing cats. I wish I were smarter.

But the book! The book was a history of the Canadian National Parks in Alberta and British Columbia. The stories of the early pioneers of the mountains were mesmerizing. I could see them riding their horses over mountains, blasting holes in mountains for railroads, and feeding grizzlies as a dare.

I read until Dad turned off the lights in our room. Then I went to the washroom and kept reading until Dad slammed his fist on the door and told me Sam needed the washroom ASAP. I got up early the following day and read some more. I read all through breakfast. I even read while we traveled. I nearly finished the darn book. But then my head and stomach started churning. I started sweating. My mouth went all sour. Then I lost my breakfast on the backside of Dad's driver seat. This put a delay in our travels.

Periodically, I would blurt out stories to my family.

"Ike Brooks rode two hundred and sixty miles of mountain trail with just one hour of sleep and almost nothing to eat just to find a doctor for his sick girl. That's over four hundred kilometers!"

"Uh, yeah. Nice."

"Banff was the first National Park in Canada, created back in 1885. It was named Rocky Mountains Park."

"Uh-huh. Yeah."

"And Field, British Columbia, was named after American Cyrus Field. The Canadian Pacific Railway wanted him to invest in the railroad. But he never did! What a waste!"

"Uh, yeah. Nice."

"And legendary mountaineer Tom Wilson! He once snowshoed over a hundred kilometers—er, seventy miles—through Pipestone Pass, going through blizzards and eight feet of snow to make it home to his little log house in Banff for a cozy Christmas supper. He lost parts off several toes because of it. But he was happy because the doctor took an equal amount of toe parts off each foot. He said he was perfectly balanced after that."

"Uh, yeah. Nice."

"And then there's Jim Brewster—!"

"Joey. Please. Look! There are the mountains!"

We all dipped our heads this way and that to look out. Faint in the distance, a bluish tint appeared slightly above the usual horizon. My first look at mountains. Unforgettable. A moment never to be repeated. An unparalleled experience.

"I have to pee," said Sam.

"We're in the mountains!" said Ellie.

"Not for another hour and a half," said Dad.

"What?" shouted Josh. "They're right there!"

"Ahh," said Dad. "Mountains are so big you can see them this far away."

"I don't need to pee anymore," said Sam.

I don't know what came over me. I don't even know how to describe it. A feeling? An amazement? A connection and realization that we were going to a special place, that this special place would take hold of me, thrill me, hurt me, belong to me. To behold these mountains for the first time was to experience a profound yearning that can never be repeated, much less understood.

Onward, we drove. Through a town called Hinton, all the way to the Jasper National Park boundary. We were flagged down by a green-shirted young man in a small building in the middle of the highway.

"Welcome to Jasper National Park! Would you like a day pass or a season pass?"

"Uh, what?" said Dad. "Uh, a season pass, I guess." He pulled out a twenty-dollar bill from his wallet.

"I'm sorry, sir, I thought you said season pass," said the man. "I'll get you a day pass instead."

"No, I want a season pass," said Dad, handing over the twenty-dollar bill.

"Yes, sir, if you could just hand over another six of these, that'd be great."

We nearly turned our vehicle around and drove home. Evidently, this was not one hundred years ago when Dad first came to the mountains. And this wouldn't be the first realization.

Dad paid and we drove on. Though, for the next ten minutes he complained about the cost of entering Jasper. It took another pee stop for Sam to distract Dad enough to enjoy where we were.

Where was that? The most beautiful place I'd ever seen. The highway curved to the left, west, and south. There was a massive lake on the right-hand side. At least, I think it was a lake. People were standing in the middle of it, with the water barely reaching their knees. We begged Dad to stop. It was Jasper Lake.

We got out and waded into the water. It was a perfect temperature. The sun bounced off ripples and into our faces, half-blinding our eyes. Outward we walked, surrounded by mountains, trees, and people. Sigh. Lots of people.

Dad said it was time to go back. Sam tripped and went under. Completely soaked. He lost his glasses in the water as well. Mom said a few words I can't repeat. After five minutes, Ellie found the glasses—by stepping on them. We all had sand everywhere as we got back to the parking lot. The sun suddenly felt excruciating. Lyda started crying. Johnny said he had a headache. Rebecca began to argue with Sam. Josh punched me hard. All because I threw a rock at his head.

Just like that, I realized that a mountain adventure with a large family would not be easy. In fact, it would be the hardest thing we ever did.

Chapter Three

Neighbors

It was past lunchtime when we pulled into the town of Jasper. Dad wanted to park near the main road next to a large grass park. But each parking spot said money was required.

"You have to pay to get into the park," said Dad. "You have to pay to park in the park. I'll bet you have to pay to sit down there too!" As you can see, money was becoming a theme for our trip.

So, we drove farther. Right out of the town of Jasper, across the main highway intersection, and onto Highway 93. The goal was to find a place to set up camp and get organized.

"There's a campground!" shouted Johnny, pointing to the right as we drove. "It's called Whistlers."

"Whoops!" said Dad. "Missed it. We'll try another."

"On the left!" said Ellie.

This time, Dad was able to steer to the left. Within a minute, we were pulling into Wapiti Campground. We were starving, tired, and grumpy.

"Hi, we're here to camp," said Dad as we pulled up to the campground office beside the road.

"What a coincidence!" said the girl at the desk. She had a thick Australian accent and even thicker hair. "Most people who come here do the same thing. Do you have a reservation?"

"Never needed that when I was here last," said Dad, looking over at Mom triumphantly.

"Oh? When was that?"

"A few decades ago, I guess. Before you were born."

"Well, crikey," said the girl, "we have a few open spots. Just for the night?"

"Um..." said Dad, turning to Mom. I could tell we were winging this trip. "We'll let you know when we're ready to leave."

"Sorry, I only have campsites for one night at a time. If you want to stay, you'll likely need to move each day."

"WHAT?" shouted Dad. "It wasn't like this last time I was here."

"Most people make reservations three months in advance," she added. "I can get you within the same general area for the next four nights. Would that work? You wouldn't have to move too far."

Dad nodded. He was too upset to say anything.

"And you're allowed up to six occupants per campsite," continued the girl, half-peeking through our vehicle window.

Instinctively, all of us kids crouched low and out of sight. This wasn't our first rodeo.

"We've definitely got six people here," said Dad, gritting his teeth, omitting the other three. It was hot outside but getting hotter in our vehicle.

I won't tell you what he said when he realized it was an extra $10 per day for the pleasure of lighting a campfire.

We drove to campsite X4 and started hauling out supplies. The sun beat down ferociously. The younger kids ran around. They got too sweaty and hot. They crashed and fought. They cried and moaned. They drank water. They repeated this process. Meanwhile, Dad, Mom, and us older kids did the camp setup.

Our tent went up after an hour of frustration. The phrase, "We can put a man on the moon but can't even set up a tent!" was shouted more than a few times. As my brothers and I unrolled sleeping bags, Mom set out a lunch of cucumbers, cheese, buns, and nuts. We sat in the blazing sun, surrounded by mountains, munching on an uninspiring lunch. It felt too hard all of a sudden. Physically difficult. Mentally impossible. How quickly hopes and expectations crash.

"So...what are we going to do?" asked Johnny.

We sat around that picnic table and, for the first time, realized that it wasn't enough to come to the mountains. You had to *do something* in the mountains.

"Whitewater rafting," said Josh.

"Too much money," said Dad.

"Up a mountain in a gondola," said Johnny.

"Nope."

"Rent mountain bikes," said Ellie.

"Yeah right."

"Shopping in the gift shops," said Mom.

"That'll be the day!"

"Rent some canoes," said Josh.

"Seriously, guys!" shouted Dad.

"Sit around and stare at others having fun," I said.

"Now you're talking."

We were at a standstill. Something had to give. We sat at the picnic table, waiting for something, anything to happen. At that moment, a rumble started. The ground began shaking. My entire body was pulsing.

"Earthquake!" said Rebecca.

The "earthquake" was a triple extra-large truck and camper winding its way towards us. Triple extra-large with a fat side of gargantuan and a heaping dose of colossal. This...thing pulled up alongside our campsite, blocking out views of Signal Mountain, which, a few seconds earlier, we were trying to enjoy.

"What's that thing?" I asked.

"It's a Fatty McButterpants," said Dad.

"Marc!" said Mom.

My brothers and I started laughing hysterically. A Fatty McButterpants!

A blonde-haired lady about my mom's age jumped out of the truck's passenger door and started making hand gestures and shouting things that could not be heard over the roar of the truck. The truck started backing up, going forward, backing up, going forward, and so on.

"Oh for crying out loud!" said Dad after a few minutes. "We can put a man on the moon but can't even park a camper. Do they need me to back the darn thing up?"

"You mean back the Fatty McButterpants up," I said, still amused.

Periodically, the man in the truck would jump out and survey the scene. He had a wide hat, a short beard, and a large belly. In and out he went, trying to back his oversized home-away-from-home into a campsite not built for such a colossal piece of equipment.

When they finally parked the camper, to my amazement, a boy about my age jumped out of the truck. He got out and sat down at the picnic table. The boy didn't look at his parents, or us, or anyone. He just had this bored expression on his face as he sat and waited for his parents to serve him. Which they did. Soon, the boy had a bounty of drinks, chocolate bars, and chips within his reach.

"I can't stand people who sit around," said Mom as we all sat around and watched.

The man and woman were anything but sedentary. They rolled around to the back of their camper and opened a massive door. The back end was a garage. The man and woman pulled out a boat on a trailer, three bikes, a canoe, three giant reclining camping chairs, a barbecue, and other miscellaneous items. When it seemed like they had finished their setup, my parents wandered over to say hello to our new neighbors.

"Hey there," said Dad. "Anything else stowed away in that camper?"

"All those kids yours?" asked the man with a grunt. "Or do you have others stowed away in your vehicle?"

Harsh.

"We just got here," interrupted my mom before my dad could snap back at the man. "We're wondering if you know of some things we could do?"

The man's wife surveyed all of us kids sitting at the picnic table. She shook her head and went inside the camper.

"Well, we know what we're doing," said the man. "It's a good idea to know this *before* you go somewhere."

This was going downhill fast.

"We," continued the man, intoning a brilliance to his words, "are doing the Family Red Chair Challenge. But that's probably out of your wheelhouse with all your kids."

"As a matter of fact," said Dad, "we're doing the challenge too." He had no idea what he was saying, but one thing I knew was that we would do this challenge, even if it killed us. A man cannot let another man outdo him. Ever.

"Ha!" laughed the man. "Well, good luck! Not that you have a chance. It's who you know, I always say. But I guess I'll see you at Edith Cavell tomorrow! Haha!"

"I guess you will," said Dad. With that, he turned around and walked back to camp.

"What are we doing?" asked Ellie.

"The Family Red Chair Challenge!" said Dad.

"What's that?" I asked.

"No clue," he replied. "All I know is we're going to win it."

"What do we do to win?" asked Josh.

"Well, let's start by finding out what an Edith Cavell is," he said.

CHAPTER FOUR

EDITH CAVELL

Edith Cavell. British nurse. Smuggled allied soldiers to safety from Belgium to the Netherlands during World War I. Executed by a German firing squad in 1915. Heroine.

Mount Edith Cavell. 3,363 meters—or 11,033 feet—high. Just south of the town of Jasper. The most prominent mountain peak entirely within Alberta. Known for the iconic 1,000-foot Angel Glacier, which hangs from the mountain, melting into Cavell Pond.

I spat out this information to my family. I was a regular Rocky Mountain historian. I mean, I read a book after all. What I didn't know was what the Family Red Chair Challenge was. For this, we had to ask at the tourist information center. Apparently, the Family Red Chair Challenge was all the rage this year.

A National Park employee explained the situation to us.

"The Family Red Chair Challenge was instituted by the Canadian government to get people to the Rocky Mountain national parks. Any family can participate. There are seven locations throughout the Rockies set up this summer with special Adirondack-style red chairs. The locations are Mount Edith Cavell, Whistlers Mountain, Opal Hills, Sulphur Mountain, Lake O'Hara..."

"Whoa! Slow down!" said my mom, desperately trying to write down all the information.

The worker, a kind-looking man named Harlan Fox-man—assuming he wore the correct nametag—paused before continuing. "The Iceline ridge by Yoho Lake, and Lake Louise. Participants must take a family picture at each red chair to prove they were there. And each red chair will have a mystery symbol imprinted on the back. All seven mystery symbols will create a secret code."

"This is great!" I interrupted.

"It sure is!" said Harlan, his short gray hair shining in the light. "That's the enthusiasm I like to see. Now, if you've figured it out correctly, the secret code from these seven symbols will lead to one bonus location. You need to be clever. Well-read even. The first family to get a picture at this bonus location wins the grand prize. National bragging rights. New camping gear. And a cool twenty-five thousand dollars! It's a big deal!"

I was jumping up and down. Now, *this* is what I envisioned a mountain trip being like!

"Let me get this straight," said Dad. "We need *everyone* in the family to be in these pictures?"

"Everyone," smiled Harlan.

"That's a little...unfair?" said Mom.

"It's what the rules are," he answered. "I didn't make them up."

"When does it begin?" I asked.

Harlan looked down at me and grinned. "Tomorrow morning! In Jasper there are several locations, including Whistlers Mountain, Opal Hills..."

"We're doing Edith Cavell tomorrow," interrupted Dad. "There's a guy I want to beat getting there."

"Good luck, guys!" said Harlan. "Maybe I'll see you around. I'm one of the employees helping to keep things running smooth, and I'll be buzzing around all the locations this summer. I'm sure I won't forget you guys. I hope you do well!"

"I'll remember you!" I said to Harlan. My enthusiasm was a bit too strong. My face turned red.

"Remember, *all* of you must be in the pictures," said Harlan, smiling pleasantly. "Good luck."

That night, my family was talking around the campfire, discussing strategy. We had long finished our meal of re-hydrated chili—Mom dehydrated all our meals before we left to save money and space. Looking over, our neighbors were just starting to cook their supper. The dad grilled massive steaks while the mom prepared corn on the cob. Their son sat around playing games on some electronic device. Their food smelled good. Too good. I couldn't help but stare at their grill. These people. They had every comfort from home and then some. But, I must say, they looked unhappy. Rare was any smile. Rare like those massive steaks on the grill, sizzling crispy with perfection and...

"We'll need to move campsites before we leave," Dad said, interrupting my stare. "This is going to slow us down."

"And I'll need help doing dishes," added Mom.

"What does it mean to find red chairs at Edith Cavell?" asked Ellie.

"I don't know," I said. "Probably you just show up there, take a picture, and then leave. Right?"

"We'd better hope so," said Mom. "Hmmph. It's not like we can climb a mountain or anything."

"Haha!" said Dad.

"Haha!" said Josh and Johnny.

"Haha!" said the rest of us.

"Haha!" repeated Dad. Only this time, we felt the awkwardness of it all.

Then we got quiet. The mountain air was cooling quickly. It was shocking how it could drop from desert heat to near-freezing temperatures within a few short hours. The sky turned a peaceful red as the sun set quickly behind a mountain. The smell of steaks sizzling over a grill mingled with the brisk fresh air and faint mist from the nearby Athabasca River. And still, we all wondered the same thing. Could we actually climb a mountain?

All of us?

"The sun's going to be up in two hours! Hurry and get moving!"

Dad was practically jumping up and down in alarm. I'm not sure what the rush was. All we had to do was get up, make breakfast, eat, do dishes, get washed and dressed, pack some gear, clean up the site, move camp, and go to Mount Edith Cavell. That'd take a couple of minutes. But, "If you're not five minutes early, you're late," is his motto.

Dreams of bacon and eggs cooking over a fire were dashed as I looked out of the tent and saw Mom preparing a giant pot of oatmeal. Oatmeal marketers must have as their slogan: *The Official Breakfast of Large Families*. I shouldn't complain. At least we had breakfast.

"Eat," said Dad. "There are kids starving in Japan."

"For Japan," I mumbled, shoving in another uninspired mouthful.

Before I knew it, we were preparing to move camp. Dad, Johnny, Josh, and I each picked up a corner of our tent, lifted it over our shoulders, and walked. We walked around the colossal camper to a spot two campsites down. Our commotion woke up our McButterpants neighbors. They clambered out and gawked at us, occasionally muttering words to each other.

After setting up a few more things at our new campground, I looked at these neighbors. The dad had started frying up bacon and eggs. The mom was combing her hair. And the boy my age was lifting weights. It turns out he could do other things besides sitting around being served.

Now, it was my turn to gawk at this. He had several dumbbells out and was breathing heavily as he lifted up and down over his shoulders. Then he'd pause and go around to his camper door. The inside of the door had a large mirror. He'd flex and stare, then go back to lifting.

Weird. At one point, he looked at me staring, shot a mean look, and I pretended to be choking. This backfired, as my dad threw water on my face, saying that would cure my coughing. I was soaked and embarrassed.

We finally left in our vehicle and prepared to see the red chairs and Mount Edith Cavell. The road was not like anything I'd ever seen on the prairies. It wound upwards in a steep back-and-forth pattern. I was told these were called *switchbacks*. Whatever they were, it sure was slow going. It took half an hour to go what should have been eight minutes of normal driving. There was no shoulder on the roadside, either. One slip and down we'd tumble to our gruesome deaths. I shuddered at the thought. Death might make us lose the Family Red Chair Challenge.

However, the drive wasn't all bad. Not at all! I noted that every minute we drove took us that much higher on the mountain. By the time we were nearing the end of the road, we could look down a valley for an endless view. Dad said it was called the Tonquin Valley. It was mesmerizing. It was terrifying. It was epic.

We were still a mile, or 1.6 kilometers, from the parking lot of Edith Cavell—in Canada, we measure by kilometers, but my dad is old and still describes distance in miles, which means I often do the math translating for everyone—when the road was abruptly closed. There were vehicles parked alongside the narrow-paved lane. Strange.

In view was, of all things, a horse stable. Horses, way up here? Dad got out to ask some people what was going on. He came back and reported the bizarre news.

"So, the red chairs are still a go," he said.

"Yay!" we shouted.

"But we can't go there," he added.

"Boo!" we all shouted.

"Why not?" I whined.

"Cause it's all a scam!" said Dad.

"How?" asked Mom.

"Yeah, well, they put the red chairs way up the mountain, on some 'third lookout' point. But you basically have to rent horses and take a horseback ride up. They created a trail to the chairs from here. I asked how much it cost to ride the horse."

"How much?" asked Josh.

"Too much," said Dad. "It'd cost the family more than a thousand bucks just to get a picture at some stupid red chairs!"

He was getting angry at the thought. I couldn't blame him. But I also couldn't give up that easily.

"Why don't we climb up without horses?" I asked.

Dad looked at me like I had two heads. That or I 100% took after my mom's side. "Because from here it'd be eight or ten miles of hiking. Well over two thousand feet up. That's insane!"

"You mean from here it would be over seven hundred meters up and twelve to sixteen kilometers of hiking?" I repeated in shock.

"I have no idea what that means!" said Dad. "All I know is this mountain is a beast. Nice heroic nurse. We'll be needing a nurse after this."

"Then we're doing it!" I interrupted. I could be stubborn. Just like my mom's side of the family, I suppose.

"Let's at least try," said Josh.

"Please, Dad?" asked Ellie.

Dad stepped out of the vehicle, said a few words not meant for younger ears, put his hands on his hips, then shook his head and returned.

"Get out," he said. "We're climbing."

After the cheers subsided, we loaded up our packs. Dad carried Lyda with a baby carrier. The rest of us had packs of water and snacks. We locked our vehicle and took our first step on the long hike. Before our second step was taken, a white truck pulled in behind us. It was our neighbors.

"Let's get going!" I shouted in panic. And we did.

After a mile of climbing the closed-off paved road, we arrived at the actual hiking trail. From there, I saw a sight I knew I could never shake. To my right was this mountain, Edith Cavell, with an immense glacier sort of floating from it. Water was rushing from the glacier towards a lime-green lake or pond. Meanwhile, loud cracks of rocks crashing down from a distance echoed in our ears. The air was cool and clear. Majestic doesn't even begin to describe it. This mountain sure put a person in his place.

Upwards, we climbed. I started using leg muscles I never knew existed. Sweat came freely. Air left quickly. This. Was. Hard.

Up rocky switchback trails we climbed. Around mountain slopes and over streams. Past little critters with round ears, we trudged. Some animals called pikas. Then, bigger, furry animals. Almost like small beavers without hard tails. These were called marmots. Some lounged around. Two marmots stood up and started boxing each other. We laughed. Then we saved our energy and climbed some more.

Into a forest, we trod. Up and up. The forest gave way to meadows. Wildflowers glistened in the sun. Still, the air became clearer. I sucked it in deeply, greedily. Through the meadows, we climbed. Then, upwards and left. Past one lookout. Past a second, too. We were now at the same elevation as Angel Glacier. And where was the third lookout?

"Look up!" said Dad.

We did. Up—way up—was a rocky peak, almost like a hill. I could see horses and people. They were smaller than ants. We had a long way to go! I groaned.

"You wanted this," said Dad, as though it was my fault this darn mountain was bigger than that one massive man in our church choir.

"I didn't know it would be this hard," I said. And I meant it.

Typically, when things get hard, we start fighting. I fight with my brothers and sisters. Mom argues with Dad. It just happens. But not this time. For some reason, we all started encouraging each other. Like the challenge brought us together.

And a good thing, too. That last part was steep! I thought we'd slip and fall to our deaths. But we didn't. The older siblings helped the younger ones. With this gritty display of teamwork, we made it to the third lookout! Best of all, we still had all our family members intact.

Our reward was to be surrounded by people. So many people. It felt like there were hundreds of horses up there. It was a regular gathering. I tried calculating how much money people were spending on horses. It was a lot.

We waited for our chance to get a picture with those two red chairs. When it was our turn, Dad handed our camera to a National Park staff member. I'd seen that person before. It was Harlan Foxman!

"So, you guys made it!" said Harlan. He looked thrilled to see us.

"Sure did," I said.

"Where are your horses?" he asked.

"We walked," said Dad, trying to point out that the horses were too expensive.

"You walked!" said Harlan. "All of you? Son of a gun! Ahh, I hope you guys win this challenge! What a family! What determination!"

He took our picture. While everyone had fancy cameras, we had an old instant camera. The kind where a picture prints out after the snap is taken. Maybe you've seen one at a museum before? Yes, we're old school. We thanked Harlan and turned to leave.

"Wait!" he said. "You need to take note of the mystery symbol!"

I looked behind the chairs. "It looks like a key." I was about to describe the key when I was interrupted.

"You guys must've rented out the stable."

It was our camp neighbor—the father, with his wife and son. The father seemed to be huffing and puffing. *He* was huffing and puffing? I can't imagine how much huffing and puffing the horse who carried him was enduring.

"Get it?" the man continued. "So many kids..."

"We climbed up!" I interrupted. I was both proud and defensive.

"You climbed up?" said the man's son. "I did my workout already today."

I think he was trying to brag. It's hard to tell with people who have more muscle than brains.

"I'll bet you carried your horse up, too, Mr. Muscles," I replied. "You know climbing a mountain is a better workout than standing at a campground and staring at yourself in a mirror every thirty seconds?" There it was. Defiant little me started things up again.

"Joey!" said my mom.

"Hey, Scott," said the boy's mom. "Just stay away from these people. They're...different. Let's get our picture and go. I want to get my fingernails done in town later today."

"What's wrong with being different?" said my mom. She looked mad.

"Oh, settle down, princess," said the lady.

"Tell your wife to zip!" interrupted my dad.

"You zip it!" said the man.

"I can't hear you over your huffing and puffing," I said.

"Joey!" repeated Mom.

"Princess," said the lady.

"Guys! Please!" shouted Harlan, waving his arms wildly. "This is not the point of the Family Red Chair Challenge!"

"I'll bet it's to make money," said Dad.

"Hey!" shouted the neighbor-dad. He seemed way too upset by these words.

"I'm sorry," said Harlan. "Really, I am. It's not my idea to charge people so much to get to these red chairs. It never used to be like this. But I'm happy you're here."

"I'm not," said the neighbor-boy named Scott.

"Oh yeah?" said Ellie, joining in the family feud festivities. "You look like you're never happy."

"Let's go," said Dad. "We'll see these people later any-way."

"Try not to lose your kids on the way down," said the neighbor-dad. This was getting old.

"Try not to crush your horse on the way down," said Dad. With that, he turned, and we followed. Down the mountain, to our vehicle. This Family Red Chair Challenge just became a bitter family rivalry.

And I was all in.

CHAPTER FIVE

OPAL HILLS

It was an awkward night at our campsite. We sat around pretending to ignore our neighbors. They sat around pretending to ignore us. We pretended to be having fun. They, well, didn't pretend to be having fun. I don't think those people knew how to pretend to smile.

It's funny how when you pretend to ignore someone, you focus on them more. Because of this, we learned a few things. For starters, the dad was named Bruno, and the mom Jacinta. I already knew the son was Scott from hearing the parents constantly dote on him. "Scott, honey, can I serve you more brisket or cheesecake? Perhaps some Belgian chocolate or fresh-squeezed lemonade? Do you need more pillows to sit on?" I think their last name was Melfort. They weren't from out West. Their dad referred to his "important" job in Ontario several times. Ottawa or something like that. He acted like a big shot. This made me more determined to beat them.

When I wasn't listening in on our neighbors' lives, I sat around rereading my book from Father Wally. I devoured stories of Jasper National Park. I contemplated adventures, names, and legends. Maybe most of all, I thought of

Father Wally's words to me. Saying others would need me, that I should be ready for this. So far, I had kick-started a family feud and got lost in a competition to the point of forgetting to have fun. I'm pretty sure others don't need me. I'm either shy, awkward, or angry. Sometimes, all three at once.

My parents were discussing what to do the next day. Mom suggested quitting this silly Family Red Chair Challenge. Dad said he'd rather die, and that he might as well teach us kids that quitting is heroic, losing is a good thing, and it's fine to let riffraff from another place walk all over you.

"We just need to go somewhere tomorrow where *that* family won't be, just to reset our focus," said Dad as he lit another marshmallow on fire. It was his eleventh in a row, which told me he was feeling stressed.

"So, where's that?" asked Mom.

"Well, I think Whistlers Mountain is what most people would do. I mean, it's what I was going to suggest. So, instead, we'll do the other red chair hike in Jasper."

"Which is..."

"Something called Opal Hills. By Maligne Lake or something."

My interest perked, and I launched into my informative, socially awkward explanation.

"Maligne Lake is famous for Spirit Island, which you can get to by boat tour. The name Maligne is French. Like malignant or evil. A priest, Father De Smet, described the river canyon that flows from Maligne Lake as that. Apparently, it's quite something. We should stop by the canyon tomorrow. Also, we should see Medicine Lake.

Medicine Lake drains every winter. There's some hidden drainage system. Water ends up in a bunch of different places! And..."

"Joey!" interrupted Dad, "I said Opal Hills."

"Popo?" said little Sam.

"No honey, Opal," said Mom.

"He means Poopoo, Mom," I told her. With that, Mom rushed Sam off to the nearest washroom. The shriek from the washroom let me know they didn't make it in time.

"What about Opal Hills?" Dad asked. Suddenly, I was the acknowledged expert. I liked that. Reading a book has many perks.

"Well, it's part of the Queen Elizabeth Range. The hike is nine or ten kilometers, er, five or six miles..."

"That's easy," said Josh.

"With lots of elevation and no zigzag switchbacks to ease your way up," I added.

"Who cares?" said Johnny as he massaged his blistered feet.

"I don't want to do it," said Rebecca. It did sound a bit much for a six-year-old.

"There are lots of flowers up there," I said. "Opal Hills was named in 1908 by the famous artist and explorer Mary Schaffer. The wildflowers reminded her of jewels."

"I want to do it," repeated Rebecca. A six-year-old is easy to convince.

"Yes, lots of flowers," I repeated. "And bears," I whispered, half-hoping she would hear the last part.

She did. "Are bears gonna eat us?" she asked with horror.

"No, dear," said Dad.

"Well..." I said.

"Joey, don't you..."

Too late, I was in it. I was in love with being the resident wise-guy.

"Bears will attack if hungry enough," I began. "But don't worry, that's rare. A grizzly bear is by far the most dangerous. And I don't just mean by size. They don't like being scared. Or shot at," I added.

"What?" said Josh. "Where are you going with this? Trying to sound smart all of a sudden."

Yes. Yes, I was. So, I continued. "In Banff, back in its Rocky Mountains Park days, a young Swedish guy named Oscar Lovgren worked near Spray Lakes. He borrowed a gun, left his work camp, and started chasing down a problem grizzly. He knocked five bullets into the bear, and it ran a short bit before keeling over. After supper, Oscar went out to retrieve the dead bear. When he got to the beast lying in a heap, the bear jumped up and swiped Oscar's face right off—crushed his skull like jelly! Killed him right then and there. They found the bear later, dead. It had five bullets in it. Tough son-of-a-guns."

"Are there grizzlies here?" asked Rebecca.

"RIGHT OVER THERE!" I jumped, pointing somewhere behind Rebecca. She fell over in fear, crying her eyes out.

I started laughing until Dad let me know that would be detrimental to my self-esteem.

"I want to go home," sobbed Rebecca.

"Any other brilliant stories, smart guy?" said Dad, turning to me.

With great intelligence comes great responsibility.

The following day, we moved camp. Like last time, Dad, my two oldest brothers, and I picked up the tent and placed it at another campsite. The problem was, despite our new location, the Melfort family were *still* our neighbors. All we did, it seemed, was rotate our way around them. Maybe this would intimidate them? Or maybe they would see it as a failed attempt to intimidate them? Who knows! All these mind games were beyond my eleven-year-old's brain power. All I know is we were gone from the campground this morning before the Melforts even woke up from their palatial Fatty McButterpants camper.

We drove north towards Jasper and then turned right towards Maligne Canyon. The plan was to stop in and tour the trails around the canyon first, which we did. There are three things I remember:

First, the water was horrific. I mean, it was intense and powerful and, to be honest, a little scary.

Second, there were a lot of people at Maligne Canyon. I was starting to understand that avoiding crowds meant going to hard-to-reach places. I am not a crowd person.

Third, I remember sitting outside the Maligne Wilderness Restaurant after we saw the canyon. We sat outside the main doors next to a pine tree while Mom made peanut butter and jelly wraps for our late breakfast. While doing this, we smelled eggs, bacon, pancakes, and everything you dream about when camping. To make it worse, the

Melfort clan walked up to the restaurant. They didn't even acknowledge us, though I know their son Scott made eye contact with me at one point. I took a dry chomp at my food and gritted my teeth. I was really starting not to like them.

"Eat," said Dad. "There are kids starving in Japan."

"For Japan," I moaned, shoving the rest of a dry peanut butter wrap into my mouth.

After Maligne Canyon we drove to Medicine Lake. What can I say? It was one of the most beautiful lakes I'd ever seen. How is it fair that so much pristine beauty is jammed into such a small area of the world? Mountains surrounded it, reflecting their grandeur on a perfect and peaceful blue water. I looked on as we drove. It was so mesmerizing. I just wanted to float in a hot air balloon and see it from on high.

Hot air balloon? I swear I saw one on the drive. And another. By the third one, I had to say something.

"Did you see...something?"

"Yes," said Dad. "I've counted at least a dozen. I have no idea what's going on. I thought stuff like that was banned in the national parks."

We pulled into the Opal Hills trail parking lot near Maligne Lake. The scene was chaos. There were hot air balloons all over, with *BMF* written on the side. Must be the company providing them. Some were taking off. Others landing. There was a sizeable makeshift vending area with a long lineup. And there was noise. Constant noise. Everywhere.

"Are we supposed to..." I groaned.

"Another money-making scheme," said Dad firmly. "That's how they get you."

"What is going on?" asked Mom. "It never used to be like this."

A National Park staff member approached us as we gazed at the balloons. She was blonde, medium build, filled with makeup, and not as friendly as Harlan Foxman. Her nametag let us know she was Kelly St. Denis. It also said she was a park manager, whatever that meant.

"Hello," Kelly greeted my parents coldly. "You need to get in line to book your balloon ride. Or several rides," she added, looking at the many kids in our family.

"Yes! Let's go!" shouted Josh.

"No!" responded Dad.

"How much?" asked Mom.

Kelly looked annoyed. We were wasting her precious time. "Three hundred and fifty dollars to get to the peak of Opal Hills."

My dad's jaw hit the ground.

"Per person," added Kelly.

My dad's entire body joined his jaw on the ground.

"The hike is too tough," said Kelly, unsympathetically. "And grizzly bears are all over. You need the balloon rides. If you don't like it, please get out of the way and let others by." With that, she turned to find other people to squeeze money out of.

"What do we do now?" asked Mom.

I scanned the crowd and noticed another National Park employee talking to folks in line. It was Harlan! I waved to him, and he came over.

"Hi, guys! I hope things have cooled off since yesterday!"

"We don't see...*them*, so yes," said Dad.

"Are you getting a few balloons today?" Harlan looked concerned as he asked.

"Harlan!" said Mom. "Why does this red chair thing cost so much money? We can't afford it!"

Harlan blushed; his kind eyes displayed honest shame. "I know. I'm not in charge. I just want to see people enjoy the national parks. Look, I'm not supposed to say this, but yes."

"Yes, what?" said Mom.

"Yes, you can climb up Opal Hills."

"We knew that," said Dad, rising to his feet.

"Well, we're supposed to tell you not to," whispered Harlan, looking left and right as he spoke.

"Why?" I asked.

"To make money," interrupted Dad.

"Well..." Harlan's face blushed again, his day's growth of gray whiskers melting into his tanned face. He was uneasy. "It will make money. I suppose that's true. However, I haven't seen any extra money come to help us service these parks. But I also need to warn you. We are in grizzly bear territory. Grizzlies love this area."

"Yes!" I shouted. "I knew it!"

"You did?" said Mom.

"Just... it'll be okay," said Harlan. "I did this hike recently, and I'm just an ordinary guy. The hike requires determination. And I would say it also requires bear spray."

"How much is that now?" asked Dad.

"Oh Marc, buy some. Aren't we at least worth not getting eaten by bears?"

"We'll be fine," said Dad. "As long as Joey doesn't open his mouth and scare everybody again. We make enough noise to scare away any bear for a hundred miles."

"Or a hundred and sixty-one kilometers," I added, turning towards the trailhead.

We were heading for another adventure.

No switchbacks on a steep trail means something called scrambling. Scrambling is climbing upwards using your hands and feet to pull you up. It's tough slogging. It makes you huff and puff. The huffing and puffing smashes your desire to talk with others.

We climbed upward and onward. Through forest with no views or inspiration to lead us to our destination. The first hour was hellacious. I don't know what that word means, but Dad said it a few times. I don't think it's a swear because Mom never told him to watch his mouth.

The path forked. We stayed right, gasping for breath as we went. Through it all, I had a bad feeling inside of me. Like we were doing something wrong, I just couldn't figure out what it was. Lost in thought, I started falling back. What a no-no.

"Joey," said Mom. "Keep up!"

Being a grumpy eleven-year-old, I slowed down. In my defense, I was cranky because I was hungry. My family started pulling ahead. Soon, I could hear them in front of me but not see them at all. After a few minutes, I heard a lonely climber coming up from behind. The person must've been out of shape. There was loud grunting as he climbed.

Curiosity got the best of me, and I looked over my shoulder.

"Ahh! Um!"

What was I supposed to say again? I said a quick prayer for help; then I remembered the words.

"Hey, BEAR!"

A grizzly was not thirty paces from me. I think I spooked it, too, because it didn't run off. It stood its ground. It even paced a bit. It was real. Game on. Rest in pieces, Joey Storthoaks.

"I won't hurt you," I said gently, trying to coax it away. I think in bear talk that means, "I'm going to hurt you," because that darn bear became more aggravated.

"Hey, bear!" I yelled again, backing away.

"Joey!" shouted Dad, coming from on high like an angel of life.

The grizzly perked up at seeing Dad run in. It jumped onto its hind legs for a moment, standing eight feet in the air, then dipped down and showed its teeth.

"Holy cow, Joey!" shouted Dad. "That's a bear! We gotta fight it!"

My mind was racing. What was that rhyme I read about? Fight? White? Flight? Goodnight? The bear stood up again. I fell backwards onto my bottom, which knocked some sense into me.

"Dad," I hissed. "Get down."

"What?"

"Black attack. Brown lay down. White good night."

"What are you saying?" asked Dad.

"Just play dead."

We both hunched over on the ground and shut our eyes. Oh my goodness, did this ever feel like the wrong thing to do. I'll bet "playing dead" sounds excellent when you're sitting at home reading about what to do with a grizzly bear encounter, sipping your grape juice and relaxing peacefully. Let me assure you, in real life, it's the last thing you feel like doing.

I counted slowly in my head. When I made it to ten, I took a peek. Just in time to see the bear wander away into the bush!

Dad opened his eyes as well. "Joey!" he said. "You nearly killed us both!"

With that, I thought of Father Wally's words of wisdom and how others would need me. Once again, I was not the solution but the problem.

"What was that 'black attack' thing you were saying?" asked Dad, this time with a gentleness that made me think I wasn't 100% in trouble.

"Black attack. If it's a black bear, you have a fighting chance against it. But only as a last option. Brown lay down. For a brown bear, you lay down and play dead."

"Well, it worked," said Dad, still shaking. "Holy cow! Did it ever! And what was that white one?"

"White goodnight. A polar bear is a carnivore. You're dead meat. Period."

Dad laughed. It was a nervous laugh. Then he got serious again. "I ran back for you. Everyone else is waiting for us. How about we...not say anything? You know, your mom might want to give up if we do. Right?"

"Right." I smiled weakly.

"And we can't let those Melfort neighbors think we're quitters. Right?"

"Right."

"And we're *not* quitters. Right?"

"Right."

I ended up telling my mom I had merely tripped backwards. This wasn't a lie. I just failed to mention that I tripped backwards because a grizzly bear looked at me like I was a juicy piece of blueberry pie.

We made our way higher and higher into some meadows. The air once again became crisp and clear. We couldn't yet see Maligne Lake from our vantage point, but we could see glorious fields of mountain flowers. This delighted Rebecca. She squealed and bounced along. Mom was getting tired and suggested we stop for lunch. She pulled more peanut butter and jelly wraps from Josh and Johnny's backpacks.

"For Japan," I said.

"You wouldn't want the kids to starve there," said Dad, shoving a dry wrap into his mouth.

I looked up at the Opal Hills' peak. It was going to take a lot of work. Worse, hot air balloons were drifting overhead. I stood on my feet and prepared to finish the hike, but a voice called from on high and nearly knocked me back down.

"Got all your kids?" echoed the faint voice.

Looking up, I saw Scott Melfort with his hands cupped to amplify his shouts. His parents stood beside him with enormous smiles on their faces.

"Please, Lord," I prayed. "I don't ask for much. Just let that boy fall out of the hot air balloon. Just this once, Lord."

My prayer went unanswered. Worst of all, Scott threw something from the hot air balloon. I think he was trying to mock us. It missed. But I went over to check it out. It was a smashed-up granola bar. No, this wasn't the worst thing. The actual worst thing was that I ate the darn thing. I was hungry. I think Scott saw this as he drifted away. He was roaring with laughter.

"Let's go!" I shouted to my family. Rage made me a leader.

We hit the peak after nearly one thousand meters of elevation gain—that's over three thousand feet. Hot air balloons drifted in and out, so we couldn't enjoy the view. We took our picture, and I looked at the secret symbol. A few mountains. That's it. Bizarre.

The trip down was peaceful. No bears. One moose in the distance. A gentle loop around a subalpine meadow. A near running pace on our descent. And no Melfort family. Life wasn't so bad after all.

CHAPTER SIX

WHISTLERS

"There's another one!" I shouted. "That's five now!"

"Six, actually!" shouted Ellie right back at me.

"Five more!" said little Sam. He had no idea what we were counting or what we were doing but wanted to join in regardless.

We were all laughing and in good spirits. Life was good. After our hike, we went swimming at Edith Lake, ate some rehydrated taco meat for supper, then headed into the town of Jasper to see the sights and sounds. As you can imagine, we parked several blocks away from downtown to avoid paying for parking.

That night, Dad said he'd take us for ice cream. We walked into the world-famous Grandma's Homemade Ice Cream shop. Then we walked out of the world-famous Grandma's Homemade Ice Cream shop.

"Let's just buy a bucket of ice cream and some cones and make our own," said Dad. "It'll be way cheaper. Paying for each cone separately is how they get you."

So, we sat on a bench overlooking streets, distant trains, and even more distant mountains. Mom was scooping up the ice cream cones. Us kids were counting people with dog strollers. Yes, we counted how many people were pushing their dogs in little strollers as if the dogs were babies—as if it wasn't the dog's wish to actually walk around.

"Wait," shouted Rebecca, ice cream covering her face and shirt. "What's that?"

A young lady walked by us. She had a baby carrier strapped on the front of her. But inside was no baby. It was a cat.

We burst out laughing. It was too much!

Little did we know that other people were snickering at us at that very moment. Had we looked carefully, we would have seen stares. We would have seen people counting as they looked our way. We would have seen smiles, scowls, and jaw drops. Seven children are a rare thing. Rarer, apparently, than treating a cat like a child.

"So where are we going next?" asked Josh, breaking into his third ice cream cone, lest we waste any and cause the children in Japan to starve.

"There's only one place left to go in Jasper," said Dad.

"You mean we have to leave?" cried Ellie.

"We can't just give up now," replied Dad. "Tomorrow, we'll see the red chairs at Whistlers Mountain, stay one more night, and then hit the road south to Yoho National Park."

"What is Whistlers Mountain?" asked Johnny.

Everyone looked at me. I shrugged my shoulders and started talking.

"Whistlers Mountain is not too high. The peak is nearly twenty-five hundred meters—er, just over eight thousand feet—up. The hike is listed as challenging. It was named

Whistlers in 1916 by Edouard-Gaston Deville because of the whistling sound from the marmots who live near the top. Whistlers Peak gives views of several mountain ranges. But mostly, it's famous for its location."

"Where's that?" asked my mom.

"Right there," said my dad, nudging his head to the right.

"That's Whistlers?" said Josh.

"Yep," I said. "And you know what that means?"

"Yes, I do," said Dad. "There's a sky tramway that leads to the summit. It means most people have to pay to get to the top."

"But we're not most people," I said confidently.

"No, we're not," said Dad. "We start climbing as soon as we finish moving camp tomorrow.

The following day, we woke up early and moved camp. To our original campsite from the first night. Still next to the Melforts and their Fatty McButterpants camper. Still next to the family we'd grown to strongly, strongly dislike—Mom says we're not supposed to hate people.

The Melforts slept in once again. All they had to do was tumble out of bed and land in the sky tramway that would carry them to the top of the mountain. Not so for us. We stretched our legs, ate oatmeal, and prepared for the most challenging hike yet. We were in it. We felt we could do anything. It was our challenge to lose.

Then the rain started.

"Maybe we should wait for the rain to stop," said Ellie.

"And give them a head start?" said Dad. Our only reason for doing the Family Red Chair Challenge now was to beat the Melforts.

"Maybe you should get off your wallet and let us ride up," said Mom.

"Let's get climbing," was his reply.

The trail began steep. There wasn't much for views, though the forest did have some streams and a neat rocky area. But the rain was making things difficult. Actually, it was making things dangerous. It wasn't surprising that we had our first serious mishap.

"Ow!" screamed Sam, slipping on a rock.

The "Ow!" turned to cries. He was hurt. When Sam slipped, his foot went backwards while his body kept moving forwards. Dad said he had a hyperextended knee. I'm not sure what that is, but it sounds hellacious.

"What do we do?" asked Mom, concern written all over her face. "Get a helicopter?"

"Yeah!" I shouted.

"I'll carry him," said Dad.

So, we shuffled loads and packs. Mom took the baby; we boys carried more supplies. The extra weight and ceaseless rain made the day perfectly miserable. We were dragging our bodies up, but our moods were sinking low.

"Dad, I'm too tired," said Rebecca.

"Well, darn it, so am I!" he snapped.

"I'm hungry," said Sam as he was carried in Dad's arms.

"You're heavy enough as it is," he said. "Just wait! You Fatty McButterpants!"

"Yeah, and kids are starving in J..." I began. Dad's look made me shut my mouth immediately.

Before too long, Johnny stumbled and cut his knee up pretty good. Our meager supply of bandages was used up. And then I slipped. My foot crashed hard, and pain shot from my big left toe straight to my head, heart, and soul. I could've wept. The rain pounding my face would've hidden all the tears anyway. I was starting to think Dad would have to call for a helicopter to rescue us, whether he wanted to or not.

"I think we need to stop," said Mom.

"And what?" questioned Dad.

"Say a prayer, maybe," she said.

We said a prayer. It was one of those prayers said in anger, where you don't feel like it, where you want to snap, where you want to scream in rage but can't because you are, apparently, talking to God.

"There, are we done now?" commented Dad.

"Lead the way, mountain man," said Mom.

Things were tense. It was getting colder now. The rain and elevation were bringing wind and chill. I started to sneeze. So did my other six siblings. Just yesterday evening, we were ready to take on the world. And now? We were defeated. It reminds me of another poetic saying from the Good Book: *Pride goeth before the fall*.

There was one positive to the cold and wind coming on strong. It meant we were getting near the top of the mountain. Hobbling, crawling, and crying our way forward, we made it to the summit.

"Of course," I said sarcastically as we tried to look at Jasper and the many mountain ranges. The mist from the rain blocked our view. We climbed all that way for zero payoff. "Of course," I muttered again.

"Let's just get a picture at the red chairs and get the heck out of here," said Dad coldly.

For that, we had to climb even further. The wind was on the point of knocking us over. We reached the red chairs, though. Other people were there, including, you guessed it.

"Crazy weather, hey?" said Mr. Melfort. He was wearing an oversized poncho, sipping what seemed like hot chocolate, and pretending to be having a rough go of it.

"It's miserable," said Dad. "We've got a few kids down for the count here."

"Good thing you have so many to take their places," quipped Mr. Melfort.

"All of us still eat less than you!" I piped up. This time, my mom didn't even try to correct me.

"Dad might be large, but I'm tough!" said the son, Scott.

"Yeah, a five-minute workout today, I'll bet," I snapped. For being a shy little misfit, my anger sure put words in my mouth.

"Bring it on!" said Scott.

"Joey, shut it!" said Dad. "Let's get the picture and get out of here."

We did just that. We ignored the Melforts, took our picture, and hobbled back to the trail.

"Dad!" I shouted. "We need to get the secret symbol!"

"It doesn't matter, Joey," he croaked at me.

Why would he say that? I didn't even reply. I hobbled over to the chairs, my toe aching pretty good now, took a peek, and saw a symbol of toes on a foot. Insult to injury. Toe injury.

When I returned to where my family was, I knew things were bad. Dad's back was aching, my foot was getting too bruised to move, and Sam was crying in pain from his knee.

"We're done," said Dad.

He stormed off in the direction of the Whistlers Mountain tramway lodge. Two minutes later, he emerged.

"Come on!" he barked.

We followed him inside the building. Next thing you know, we were heading down, on the tramway. Dad had broken the bank. He had spent money. The end of the world was upon us.

It was a miserable ride down.

That night, we huddled inside our tent. Rain was still pouring down. We ate peanut butter and jelly wraps since it was too challenging to cook outside. Everyone was cold and dreary.

"We're finished," Dad announced suddenly.

"No!" I shouted.

"Yes!" Mom contradicted.

"Joey, admit it, this is too tough," said Josh.

"We can do it!" I said.

"Stop being a brat," said Ellie.

"You stop being a brat," I replied. Not the best comeback ever.

"Joey, look what you're getting us into," said Mom, her voice escalating. "*We'll* do the parenting here, thank you very much. Just shut your mouth and eat supper."

"For the kids starving in Japan," I mumbled.

Mom forced us all to drive to the Wapiti Campground showers that night. She said the warm water would heat our bodies in preparation for the cold night. I took a thirty-second shower and then waited half an hour for my mom and sisters to shower and dry their hair. As I sat waiting impatiently, Scott Melfort walked in.

"Hey," he said, smirking.

"Hey," I said, scowling.

"You guys can't keep up with us," said Scott. I swore he tried flexing his skinny little arms as he said that.

"Not anymore," I announced. "We're heading home."

"Quitters," he said.

My blood boiled. Quitters? Is that what we were? Or were we being smart? Safe? Knowing our limits?

No, Scott was right. We were quitters. One bad day. To give up after one day was to quit. I wasn't going to have any of it.

"We'll see about that," I mumbled to Scott. He glared at me. I glared at him.

I wasn't ready for this to end.

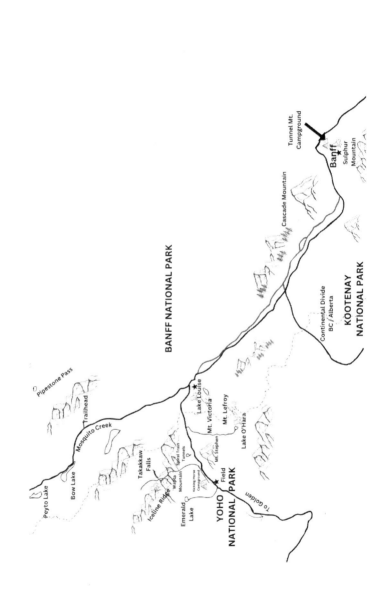

CHAPTER SEVEN

YOHO

The following day, the sun rose. That sounds like an obvious statement. But when you endure a day of solid rain, chill, and desolation, it seems a miracle to see that sun again.

Sunshine brings many things. Warmth. Light. Hope. For whatever reason, I was feeling it. I was feeling defiant. I was feeling hopeful. I was feeling like this wasn't the end. And I knew I had to take matters into my own hands because, for my parents, this was the end. They were planning on heading back home to Saskariver—all of us. There were too many wounds to lick and aches and pains to heal.

None of us were dead. Sam's knee was feeling better. My toe didn't need amputation or anything. Nothing that a simple day of rest couldn't take care of. Still, we packed up our tent, shook out the water as best we could, and stowed it in our vehicle. The oatmeal tasted good this morning. I was getting chipper. Everyone else was silent and somber.

"We're not really going home now, are we?" I asked, scared of the answer to come.

"I'm afraid so," said Mom softly.

"But can we..." I started.

"No."

Looking up toward Signal Mountain, the sun clear over it now, bringing peace and clarity, I pondered what could be done. How could I extend this trip, I wondered.

"Can we at least take a different way home?" I asked.

"Why?" said Dad.

"Um..." My mind raced. I hadn't thought of that part yet. My brain flipped frantically through the pages of *Rocky Mountain Stories*. It landed on a particular page. My only hope. "I'd like to see David Thompson country at least."

"What about David Thompson?" he asked.

"He's a legend!" I insisted, gathering my courage. "David Thompson mapped almost two million square miles of land. He's the greatest there's ever been! And he did most of this with his wife and thirteen children! We need to go see where he explored."

"Where's that?" asked Mom. "I thought he explored all over."

"Yes, but there's a highway that heads home," I said. "We go down the Icefield Parkway, then turn onto the David Thompson Highway. It'll take us straight to Rocky Mountain House past all his ranges. From there we can go home quickly.

"It's on the way home, then?" said Dad.

"Of course," I said.

Dad was stuck. I could tell he was interested in seeing a few new things. I could also tell that he had firmly told us we were heading straight home. Sometimes, you have to choose between adventure or your pride.

"Let's just do it," said Mom. Marriage is a beautiful, correcting thing.

"Fine," agreed Dad.

"Yay!" shouted all of us kids.

We finished packing up. Turning my head, I looked up at Whistlers Mountain. Trams were going up and down. This mountain almost did us in. But I still had hope. Then I got that feeling of sadness you have when you must say goodbye to a special place. Jasper National Park is such a place. I wanted to come back, and I hadn't even left yet.

We drove south down the highway on what is called the Icefield Parkway. Some say it is the most beautiful drive in Alberta. What an underwhelming thing to say. Others say it is the most beautiful drive in Canada. This is more accurate. And finally, some people say it is the most beautiful drive in the world. I would agree with this.

We stopped briefly to see Athabasca Falls and Sunwapta Falls. I couldn't tell you which is my favorite. Further south, we drove. Something remarkable started happening. The mountains seemed to grow. Larger and larger. With more snow and glaciers. The weather cooled. Our vehicle started grinding. We were gaining altitude. Before I knew it, we were driving almost to the top of the mountains, looking far below onto Beauty Creek. Tangle Ridge was on the other side of the highway, looking majestically treacherous.

Dad gripped the steering wheel as we continued to climb. Around Tangle Creek Falls, past the Columbia Icefield Skywalk, where people paid to walk on a glass platform hundreds of feet over a valley, and then down to the Columbia Icefield Glacier. I cannot describe the magnitude of this place. I only hope everyone in the world gets a chance to visit. Wait, I hate crowds. Never mind that last statement.

Onward, we drove. I started getting nervous. I knew my pathetic plan was ready for takeoff. I took a breath from the back of the vehicle and called out, "Look ahead on the right. Far ahead *on the right*. I think there's a grizzly bear!"

"Where?" shouted my siblings.

"Again?" said Dad.

"What do you mean *again*?" asked Mom.

"Um," said Dad. "Nothing."

"I don't see it," said Ellie.

"Just keep looking to your right," I pleaded as we drove. "Far on the right."

Dad tilted his head, trying to get a glimpse. "I don't see it."

"It might be!" I said again. "Just on the right."

After an awkward minute of questions, my family finally decided that I was out of it. That I probably saw a stump or rock. That I had rocks in my head and needed to stop talking.

We drove on in silence. The views continued to stun. We saw White Pyramid, Howse Peak, and Mount Patterson Glacier; it was a glorious drive. Soon, signs for Peyto Lake, with its famous wolf-head face, came into view. It was named after Wild Bill Peyto, one of the early legends of the Rockies. I braced myself as we drove on. I think even Dad would understand that this famous lake wasn't, in fact, part of the road to David Thompson Country.

"Where's the turn to Rocky Mountain House?" asked Dad finally.

"It'll be on the *left*," I said quickly. A little too quickly.

He became suspicious. "So how far away are we from it?" he asked, his voice lowering.

"Maybe half an hour or more."

"There's no way!" he burst out. "We still have another half hour to go?"

"Not quite," I said sheepishly.

"What do you mean?"

"Well, we're over half an hour away."

"And?"

"And getting farther away with each minute we drive..."

Dad slowed down the vehicle and pulled right into Bow Lake's parking lot. "Let me see a map!"

Mom handed him a map. We kids jumped out of the vehicle. The boys ran to the bush; the girls ran to the outhouses. Mom, Dad, and the baby remained in the vehicle.

"What was that all about?" Josh whispered as we returned to the vehicle.

"Do you want to go home?" I asked.

"No!"

"Then just stick with me."

Returning to the vehicle, Dad spoke up. "It seems we've gone too far. Almost like a mysterious bear kept us from making our turn." He glared at me. "We're turning back!"

"No!" I shouted, looking up to the mountains in desperate prayer.

"Joey!" said Mom.

"Look!" I shouted, pointing to the highway.

"Not that again," said Dad. But he gave in and turned his head.

A large, colossal, gargantuan Fatty McButterpants camper drove by heading south. We looked out and saw the Melforts pointing at us and laughing. Scott had his fist in the air like he'd just won the Stanley Cup. They honked twice and kept on driving.

Dad stared as the camper drove out of view. The sun sparkled in the gentle wind, making the moment like a segment of a dream.

"Get in the vehicle," he spoke.

We did just that. Dad pulled out onto the highway. Heading south.

"Where are we going?" asked Mom.

"Wherever they're going," he said. Then he looked at the rearview mirror and smiled at me. I smiled back. "We aren't quitters, after all."

"Kicking Horse Campground is where the CPR workers camped in 1884 while they built the railroad through the Kicking Horse Pass. It's called Kicking Horse because, in 1858, geologist James Hector's horse kicked him in the chest near here. The name stuck."

"Uh-huh," said Mom as we drove on.

"And we're now in the province of British Columbia. The great divide splits Alberta and British Columbia. So, now all the rivers will flow to the Pacific Ocean from here."

"Uh-huh."

"And the National Park is called Yoho. 'Yoho' is a Cree word meaning amazement or awe. The park was formed in 1886."

"Uh-huh."

"And..."

"Joey!" said Dad, shattering my moment. "I need to focus so I don't miss my turn."

With that, he turned right and headed down to Kicking Horse Campground. Of course, we didn't have a reservation. However, they had a few campsites set aside on a first-come, first-served system. We took a site and were told to request it again by 11:00 a.m. the following day. We could do this for several nights. Perfect.

Everything was set up. Food was served—rehydrated chili again. And then we wandered about. The mountains seemed to close in on us here. They were always a stone's throw away.

"What are we doing tomorrow?" I asked.

"Well, we're right next to a red chair," said Dad.

"Will it be easy?" asked Ellie.

"If you have money, probably," said Dad.

"You'll be thinking of the Iceline Trail by Yoho Lake and Takakkaw Falls," I said.

"Sure am," said Dad. "We'd better get to bed early; I assume we'll have some climbing tomorrow."

A large, colossal, gargantuan Fatty McButterpants camper pulled into our campground just as he spoke. The occupants of the truck were eating ice cream cones and looking miserable. When they noticed us, they started pointing and laughing.

I swear we were the only reason they ever smiled.

"We'll see who gets the last smile," I said quietly. "We'll see."

I slept well that night.

Chapter Eight

Iceline Trail

I t's me here again. Live. In the flesh. Behind bars. In jail. I'll bet you forgot that I'm still here telling the story.

Any guesses yet why my family is in jail? Wrong. Not for murdering the Melforts. However, the thought did enter my mind more than once. You know, a subtle push off the side of a mountain. A touch of rat poison on their sirloin steaks. Baiting a grizzly bear, or worse, Peaches-n-Salami, into their Fatty McButterpants camper, shutting the door, and walking away. I know I shouldn't say such things.

The guard brought us food, finally. How about more of the guessing game? What do you think the food was? No, it wasn't peanut butter and jelly wraps! That would be cruel and unusual punishment. Not simple ham sandwiches, either. He brought us catered food from a local Banff restaurant—barbecued chicken with killer sweet-and-sour sauce, French fries, garlic toast, and salad. I haven't eaten this well since I left Saskariver. For the starving children in Japan! Maybe being a criminal isn't so bad?

"I'm thankful I homeschool," I say to Mom suddenly, with ketchup still on my face.

"Aww, that's nice," she says. "Why do you say that now?"

"Because if I was in real school, when it starts up in the fall I'd have to write a 'what I did last summer' assignment. I wouldn't want to tell everyone I was a prisoner in jail."

A prisoner in jail. It's sinking in again. Honestly, sitting here makes me realize how much I miss Saskariver. It makes me want to philosophize about life, or whatever that word is where you have smart thoughts. And since I read a book recently, it goes without saying that I *am* pretty smart. Philosophize? Falafel-ize? Full-awful-eyes? Whatever the smart-thinker word is.

I've been thinking about how my hometown of Saskariver is simple. There are open fields, scattered forests, big skies, bigger hearts. It's a simple place with simple people.

I think of the Ducklac twins. Wandering my hometown each day. Friendly as heck. Talking your ear off. Once, they saved a lost puppy roaming the streets. Just scooped the dog up and carried it from house to house, looking for the owners. They walked for eight hours straight. By the end they were totally bonded with that puppy. Turns out the dog belonged to them. Their dad had brought the dog home as a surprise; it escaped, and they found it anyway—just legends.

I think of Green Truck Guy. The old guy who drives through town three times a day. Slower than molasses going uphill in the wintertime is what they say. He always has a parade of vehicles behind him. They can't pass him. I think he delights in this. It's his purpose in life. The other drivers now realize that you can either accept the slower pace and enjoy the day or rage at the loss of a few minutes.

I think of Olaf. An old man who's building a rock house in the woods near Saskariver. He's been at it for over thirty years. I once visited his half-finished house. I asked him if he'd ever finish the house before he died. He said probably not, and he wasn't concerned. It's going to be for his son, and then his grandkids, and so on. Just a place on Earth. Where there is no rush to do something, go somewhere, change something that doesn't need changing. A simple life. A good life.

I think of Marty the Moose, Mustache the lumberyard worker, Miss Fancy Spudd the librarian, Honk'n the carpenter, Buffalo the...whatever he does for a living. I'll bet these Saskariver folks would be labeled crazy misfits by much of the world. I say, who wants to be normal according to what the world thinks? As I saw at Takakkaw Falls, acting like others isn't always desirable.

All this philosophi...erzing...*thinking* is making me hungry again. I'd better get back to my story.

The next morning, we drove on the road to the Iceline Trail. What an experience. Once you pass the confluence for the Yoho and Kicking Horse rivers, you drive through the steepest road switchback I've ever seen. *If* you survive this, you will soon see the most stunning waterfall I've ever known. Takakkaw Falls.

Takakkaw Falls is alongside the road. It's relatively easy to find. Getting there requires no physical exertion. And it is beautiful. Easy and beautiful means that people flock to it. I'm happy they do. But sometimes these stunning places bring out the worst in people.

"Look at that!" said Josh as we walked the path near the picnic area. It was the path that eventually led to our trail.

"Hellacious," I replied.

We saw some tourists taking rude pictures, horsing around, messing with the outhouses, leaving garbage, and drawing graffiti. A group of young men laughed loudly, swearing and acting like they owned the place. They weren't even looking at Takakkaw Falls. I felt embarrassed.

"Kids, stay close," said Dad. He felt uncomfortable. "I know where I'm going."

He led us straight to another area where several families were having a rowdy picnic. These people were throwing rocks at nearby ravens. Actually, they were baiting the ravens with food so that they'd come closer, and then they'd hammer rocks at them. It was a game to them until a raven snapped and attacked one of the parents. Ravens are big birds. The attack left a small trail of blood. Good for the raven.

"You know where you're going, hey?" said Mom.

"Well, darn it!" said Dad. "It's all distracting! This stupidity is normal here! Why can't people be normal like us!"

"Look!" interrupted Sam, "Lyda has chocolate on the back of her shirt!"

"That's not chocolate!" said Mom, rolling her eyes.

We "normal people" waited while a diaper change was made. It gave me time to think of what my dad said. This beautiful place... It was like all this outward beauty in nature revealed rotten inward hearts. I suppose it's complicated. I prefer simple.

I tried to shake off what I saw and turned my eyes to the mountains across from Takakkaw Falls. What I saw was even more devastating. A gigantic roller coaster snaked upwards to the top of a mountain. A roller coaster on the side of a mountain?

"So that's the gimmick here," said Dad, looking up at a mountain called *The President*. "Well, let's go."

We walked across the road to where crowds were gathering. There, we saw Kelly, the Parks Canada employee. Harlan wasn't around.

"Hi, guys!" said Kelly. "What do you think?"

"What *is* it?" asked Mom.

"It's the BMF Red Chair Coaster! You can get a lift up and down the mountain to the red chairs."

"Let me guess, for a small fee of fifty dollars per person," said Dad.

"Seventy-five, actually," said Kelly.

"But...why?" asked Mom.

"Isn't it great that people get to go up mountains? It makes us all one with nature."

"I don't think throwing a coaster up a mountain makes us one with nature," said Dad. "It makes us against it."

"Oh, it's not forever, I think," Kelly replied, smiling. "The government's Family Red Chair Challenge is temporary. Maybe they'll move the roller coaster to another mountain next year! I hope!"

"So, where's the trail to get to the chairs?" I interrupted.

"You can start at the main trail—lots of switchbacks. But you have to take a longer way to get to the top. Go left at the junction. It'll take you by Yoho Lake, up some forest, and then to the Iceline Trail. Honestly, spend the money on the coaster!"

"No thanks," said Dad.

"I'll bet Harlan doesn't like it either," I blurted out.

Kelly's eyes narrowed. "Harlan doesn't like much of what we do. He's not a *team player*." With that, she turned her head, snapping her blonde ponytail at us, and walked away.

"Okay, Joey," said Dad. "What are the specs and all?"

"Far and hard," I said. There was nothing else to add.

We stretched our legs and headed up. Thankfully, our injuries weren't a significant factor. The hike was challenging enough without additional aches and pains.

Through the forest, we climbed. Switchbacks, streams, and scenic views kept us gasping for air. I wondered if my family would turn on me for baiting them to endure more hiking. We'd probably be home by now if it weren't for me.

"The Storthoaks family never gives up," said my dad suddenly as we grunted forward. I'm unsure if he meant to say it out loud or not.

"The Storthoaks family never gives up," I repeated. I'm unsure if *I* meant to say it out loud or not.

"The Storthoaks family will not be outworked," said Dad, building on his first call.

"The Storthoaks family will not be outworked," I said. This time, Sam and Rebecca joined in.

"The Storthoaks family never leaves someone behind," said Dad.

"The Storthoaks family never leaves someone behind," repeated everyone (except baby Lyda).

"The Storthoaks family enjoys a good hike and rehydrated chili..."

"The Storthoaks family enjoys a good hike and rehydrated chili."

"The Storthoaks family sets the pace..."

"The Storthoaks family sets the pace."

"The Storthoaks family forgives the Melforts..."

"The Storthoaks family..."

It got quiet. What did Dad say? After all that happened with the Melforts? Was he a hypocrite? Did he have a change of heart? I looked up at Dad as he plowed ahead with Lyda on his back. At that moment I realized he was a man worth following.

"The Storthoaks family forgives the Melforts," I stated. Alone.

"The Storthoaks family forgives the Melforts," added the rest of my family.

I smiled. It was easy to say, not so easy to do.

We arrived at Yoho Lake. Picture emerald-green water, so clear and calm that you can see the perfect reflection of Wapta Mountain, like a crown on a rook in chess, touching both the heavens and the waters below. A loon floated on by. Pine trees swayed gently. Two gray jays fluttered nearby, hoping for food. We kept our peanut butter and jelly wraps to ourselves. This beat any mountain coaster I could think of.

"Dad?" I said, breaking the silence.

"Yes?"

"What if we meet the Melforts at the red chairs again?"

"We take our picture and come back down."

"What if they start bugging us again?"

Dad sat still for a moment, lost in thought. "I'll just point and say there's a grizzly bear on the right. That seems to solve problems." With that, he stood up to indicate it was time to move on.

The rest of the hike was a blur. Being overwhelmed with beauty will do that to you. It gets dizzying. The Iceline Ridge carried us to a viewpoint above Takakkaw Falls. We could see its glacier, Yoho Valley, and the peaks of many surrounding mountains. Unfortunately, before long, we could hear and see the crowds traveling up the mountain coaster. Why, oh why?

The red chairs were a party zone. Someone was playing music. Others were laughing, singing, and eating. Garbage was everywhere. I was upset.

We got our picture. I checked the secret symbol; it was a rock. Or a diamond. I hadn't even started putting these symbols together yet in my mind. They were so disconnected. It was best to wait until we had all seven.

As we turned to leave, up the coaster came our dear friends, the Melforts. The mom and dad were eating chips. Scott was eating a hamburger. Where he got it, I couldn't say. We tried to duck away, but they spotted us first.

"Got 'em all?" said Mrs. Melfort. This family really needed a new way to start a conversation.

"Yes," said Dad.

"Wouldn't want you to pay for them to go up and down," said Mr. Melfort. "They just aren't worth it."

My dad's eyes bulged. But he didn't say anything. I did.

"There's a grizzly bear over there on the right!" I shouted.

The Melforts jumped ten feet, which was no easy task for the large mom and dad. Other people started screaming and running around. Chaos was coming. So, we snuck away, laughing.

From our trail, we could hear more yells and shouts. Let the crazy scene figure itself out. We were heading for a peaceful trek down.

And it was.

CHAPTER NINE

LAKE O'HARA

Have you ever been excited about something, can't wait for something, have done nothing but think about something, and when it arrives, you're a hot mess and can't enjoy it? Like that one Christmas a couple of years ago. For three months, I counted down the days, put up decorations, baked cookies, heck, I even unwrapped my presents, snuck a look, and rewrapped them. Then Christmas came. I was grumpy all day. I don't know why. It made no sense. Everyone else was bubbling with the festive spirit. I was snapping and crying and being a brat. It just happened. It can't be explained.

There we were at Kicking Horse Campground. We had four out of seven red chair pictures. We were in it. And the next day was taking us to a stunning place. I should've been happy. Actually, I should've been asleep. But I wasn't. I was getting *them blues*, as my grandpa might say.

It was about two in the morning. Our tent was crammed with people, as it always is. The temperature was dropping. I like sleeping in the cold weather, all cozied up in my sleeping bag. And I was exhausted from the day's hike. Everything was perfect for me to be sleeping.

Except I wasn't. For starters, my dad was snoring.

It sounded between a teenager revving his pickup truck's oversized engine and a dozen tubas spinning around in a monsoon. I couldn't handle it. So, I did something brave. By brave, I mean stupid. I picked up my pillow and threw it at Dad.

"Whoa!" said Dad, raising his head in terror.

But as soon as he raised his head, he lowered it back on his pillow and continued sleeping. Thankfully, this time, his snoring was cured. Too bad my pillow was over there.

I lay my head on the cold ground and listened to something other than Dad's snoring. I heard a train echo through the spiral tunnels from one of the nearby mountains. I listened to the roar of the Kicking Horse River ramble west to the Pacific Ocean. I could feel its power vibrate through the ground to where I lay, lulling me like a mother rocking an infant child. And still, I couldn't sleep.

I exited my warm sleeping bag and slipped out of the tent. The chill shocked me and almost made me jump back inside. I wandered down the campground road—just a little way. Looking up, I saw a sight. Thousands—millions—of piercing white stars gracing a clear black sky. Diamonds in the night, broken up only by the silhouette of glorious Mount Stephen. I was in a special place. But I couldn't shake my growing unhappiness.

What came next did shake me. I heard a loud sound. A hoot of some sort. It startled me more than I'd like to admit. I raced back to our tent, zipped up the door, and hid in my sleeping bag. The hoot came again. I knew that sound. It was of a great gray owl. Some say their call is an omen of bad luck. Others say a beloved deceased family member is watching out for you. All I know comes from a story someone from Saskariver once told me. It was winter, and Dad and I were picking up some wood at the Lumber Coop. One of the workers, a friendly guy nicknamed Mustache—hopefully that was his nickname—was telling us of a great gray owl he once saw.

"I was driving home late at night once. Yeah. Had to slam on my brakes. Guess what was in front of me? A great gray owl. As big as you could imagine. The thing looked up and stared at me. Stared me down, yeah. Like I was in his territory and needed to go. Scared me a bit. I looked down, and he had his talons jabbed into a giant snow-white rabbit. The owl looked at me to make sure I was watching, freaky goblin, then dropped his head down and bit that darn rabbit's head right off. He looked back at me with the rabbit's head dangling from his beak and flew off into the night. Yeah. Bad stuff. Then guess what? I got a splinter in my finger the next day. Bad stuff, for sure. Yeah. But it's not all bad. Made these mittens here using the rabbit fur he left behind. Oh yeah."

I fell asleep. My dream was of headless rabbits coming to cuddle me.

"Get up, Joey!"

The pot of oatmeal was getting dangerously close to being empty. And Sam was eyeing up another bowlful. I didn't care. I didn't want any more of that mushy gloop. The kids in Japan could starve for all I cared.

"Joey!" called Mom again.

No response. If I had to eat another spoonful of that oatmeal, I might call the government and complain about child cruelty.

"Joey, this is your mother. Please get up!" she pleaded with me.

No response from me.

"Joey! Get the heck out of bed right now!" barked Dad.

Whoosh. Up and out of the tent in three seconds flat. It's not right to disobey Mom. But it's downright hazardous to disobey Dad. I stepped out of the tent and jumped into the day.

"Well, good morning, sunshine," said Josh with no shortage of sarcasm.

I growled back.

"Lake O'Hara today! They say it's a piece of heaven there," said Ellie.

I gave her a look that a demon would be proud of.

"Get dressed. We're going," said Dad.

I did as I was told. But I didn't do it happily.

We turned east along the Trans-Canada Highway towards the Lake O'Hara Road. As we did, Dad asked me the usual questions.

"So, what can you tell us about Lake O'Hara, Joey?"

"It's a place on Earth," I snapped.

With remarkable patience, Dad continued, "Any cool stories? Where do you think the red chairs are?"

"To start, you can't drive there," I began. "You have to rent a seat on a bus months in advance, or you have to walk eleven kilometers...which is almost seven miles for old people who don't know the difference."

"I know what kilometers are!" said Dad, annoyed. "They were invented by the government in the 1970s to control people. And don't you dare talk to me like..."

"Marc!" interrupted Mom. "We have to walk nearly seven miles to get there?"

"That's just to get there," I said. "Then who knows where the chairs are? Up a mountain? At another lake? At the top of another roller coaster? Some place where big, stupid families can't reach them."

We pulled into the Lake O'Hara parking lot. Full. We waited thirty minutes for a parking spot to open. Another vehicle tried to wedge into our spot, but Dad held his ground and muttered a few unpleasant things at the driver before pulling in. Public parking brings out the best in people.

"Let's pack our swimming gear, too!" said Josh as we loaded our backpacks for the trek. "I could use a swim."

"You smell like it," I said quickly.

"Fine, we'll pack our swim gear," said Dad before turning in my direction, "but any complainers will be left out of the water."

It was a long road. Uphill. Uninspiring. The kind of hike that makes a grumpy person want to light the Earth on fire, fly into space, and never return. The day was getting hotter, too. Lyda filled a diaper. Then another one. Too much oatmeal, probably. This was getting ridiculous. We approached Lake O'Hara three hours later, just in time for Lyda to complete the diaper hat trick.

"This is stunning!" said Ellie. "Oh look at how the trees break the gap between the water and the mountains!"

"Ya seen one lake, ya seen 'em all," I said.

"Oh...go away!" she replied.

"Hey, enough!" insisted Dad. "Let's go see where the chairs are."

Looking at the crowds near a large lodge-type building, I could tell instantly what the gimmick was. Canoes!

"We get to paddle a canoe to the chairs!" said Josh.

"Yeah right," I said.

"Joey!" said Mom.

"Oh boy...canoes," said Dad. "I'll go see what's up."

He walked over to the center of the hubbub and talked with someone for a while. Then I saw him talking with another person. He looked animated. Upset even. Finally, Dad came back shaking his head.

"The red chairs are out in the lake's center," he began, "set up on an island of sorts. We can rent a BMF-brand canoe to get there, but we're only allowed one trip out with the canoe before we have to return it. We'd need to rent three canoes! And they aren't cheap!"

"See?" I said.

"Joey!" said Mom.

"Oh, and you'll be happy to know that the Melforts are here, renting a bright-red canoe at this very moment. They argued with a park employee over the canoes not having enough padding. And Mr. Melfort says he hopes we don't leave any kids behind." Dad let us make a few angry faces before continuing. "I have a plan. I think we can make it out there if..."

"If what?" said Mom. "It's not like we can swim there! Haha."

"Haha!" said Dad.

"Haha!" said the rest of us.

"Marc!" Mom said. "You're not serious!"

"Oh, come on now," he replied. "We'll rent a few life jackets for the youngest kids or borrow the ones that people seem to be leaving on shore when they head out. We'll leave from the closest point, right over there. I can put the camera in one of those watertight bags we keep our wraps in. Maybe add an empty water bottle to help it float. And..."

"Marc!"

"Let's go to these bushes here. Girls on the left. Boys on the right. See you in a few. Now go get dressed."

Five minutes later, we were on the shores of Lake O'Hara, about to dip our toes in the water. Lyda, Sam, and Rebecca wore life jackets. The rest of us kids could swim the short-ish distance to the chairs. What's the point of taking swimming lessons every year if you can't actually swim?

We kids were fine swimmers. But as we were about to find out, the same could not be said for all the adults.

CHAPTER TEN

LAKE O'HARROWING

I have vague memories of a hotel trip from a past vacation. It was one of those hotels where you pay a lot of money to get a crummy room. Why? Because the hotel has a pool and waterslide.

We were happy to swim all day, all evening, and then all next morning. I went up and down that waterslide over sixty times. I was going for the world record. What the world record was, I couldn't tell you.

I remember Mom in the little pool with the younger kids. And Dad? He came down to the pool eventually. Standing near the edge of the water, we called to him.

"Come in! Come in!"

"I float like a rock!" he would say, laughing, before easing himself into the water.

I don't remember much else other than he didn't swim for long and stayed in the shallow end of the pool. But he could swim. He was there. Right?

There were twenty or so canoes out on the water of Lake O'Hara, shuttling families back and forth. The island red chair location was a hit, if you had money. For us, we were about to find out what we were made of. Seven kids swimming out to get a stupid picture? Sometimes, adventure makes little sense. But it's still adventure. You're still lapping everybody sitting on the couch at home.

A cold mountain lake is not so bad once you get used to it. Sure, your body is cold. But the sun beats down on your head and shoulders; it reflects off the water into your face. Once your body starts moving, you heat up just fine. Besides, as my mom always says, kids don't get cold when swimming.

My oldest brother, Johnny, was on his back, doing some elementary backstroke. He had the camera in a water-tight bag, resting between his chin and neck. No problem.

My next brother, Josh, was a sight. Being the best swimmer in the family, he took the baby. Lyda had a life jacket. To be safe, Dad managed to swipe another life jacket for Josh. Josh was on his back, with Lyda on his chest. It was the life-saving backstroke. Josh made it all look easy. The two were giggling as they went. No problem.

Ellie and I flat-out swam—no life jackets. No problem.

Rebecca and Sam each had life jackets. The two doggy-paddled forward, laughing as they went. No problem.

Mom was in the front next to Josh and Lyda. She had no life jacket but managed to doggy-paddle her way forward easily. No problem.

Dad was in the rear. He was to make sure us younger kids were fine. He doggy-paddled forward as well. I didn't notice him much. I was focused on our target and enjoying myself. Once, I looked back and saw his eyes and mouth barely above water. But that wasn't a big deal. Except that the next time I looked back, he was looking tired. Too tired. Problem.

"Dad?" I called out once. He was twenty strokes away, dragging down our pace.

"Yep," he answered. "Just keep going."

I did keep going for another minute. There were canoes far off to the right. One was drifting a little closer to us. I didn't get a good look at it. I looked to the left. The distant shore was empty of people. I imagined moose or bears enjoying the water away from the crowds. Wildlife has much more sense. I imagined birds swooping and playing near the water's edge. I saw a bird do just that. Not an ordinary-sized bird. A big one. Like a giant owl. Like a great gray owl.

Cough!

I turned my head back, and my skin vibrated instantly and uncontrollably. I could see my dad's arms, the top of his head, and nothing else. He was struggling to breathe. He was drowning.

"Dad!" I called, turning my body around to face him.

His arms splashed, sending white water in a rage around his body. One splash revealed his head coming up for a gasp before sinking.

"Dad!" I called, shouting this time, hoping someone else would notice.

No one was paying attention. Dad splashed a few more times, though with less force than before. Finally, I just let it all loose.

"Help! HELP! *HELP!*" I screamed. This got attention. Unfortunately, my older siblings were far ahead, out of reach. I felt alone. With a drowning father.

I swam over to Dad. He was only getting air in small spurts now. Reaching him, I tried to pull him up while he tried to support himself on my shoulder. All this did was send me below the water. An entire foot down. I shook him off and shot to the surface, greedy for air. I was useless to help.

The situation was quickening. Like a giant boulder tumbling down a mountain, picking up speed on its way, racing towards a sudden and devastating impact. For some reason, my mind drifted. I could see *it* all happen, whatever *it* was that was happening.

I was at a funeral. A most unhappy, overwhelming funeral! Father Wally was talking, but I wasn't listening. People were coming over and saying things. I wanted them to leave me alone. To never come back. To a cemetery, we walked. A few more unheard words were said. The hoot of an owl. In an instant, it was all over. Empty. Afraid. Confused.

"What now?" came a voice, interrupting my thoughts.

The voice came from a shiny red canoe. There were three passengers on board. They seemed unconcerned, like they thought we were joking around in the water, splashing and frolicking freely.

I grabbed my dad's arm again and lifted it with all my strength. Doing so sent me underwater. My arms were raised over my head, just above the water. I lifted my dad's right hand further until it grabbed the side of the canoe.

Just enough. The man who spoke in the canoe became concerned. He stood up and shouted.

"Hey!" he yelled, standing up. "Don't do that!"

His standing sent the canoe off balance precisely when my dad gave his last effort to pull his head above water. The canoe pulled toward Dad. One side went down, the other up. The man standing lost balance and started falling. The canoe slipped and rotated, straight at Dad. I was still under as it flipped over, right on top of me. Three people went crashing down into the water. The smallest one—thankfully—landed on me. It hurt. I saw stars. Was it the impact? Or that I hadn't had a gasp of air in far too long? I kicked under the water, searching for a place to find the surface. I had to swim down and around before I could come up. As I pushed to the surface, the sun's light leading me forward, I started taking water. My head pounded. Too much pressure. Too much...light...floating on harmless and free and...

Whoosh! My head bounced up, and I coughed, sputtered, drank in water and air, and coughed some more.

I flailed around, weak and weary; I managed to grab onto the canoe floating upside down. It was slippery and near impossible to hold on to, but it was something. Just enough for me to gather my wits.

Shaking my head of water, I saw three people in life jackets splashing beside me in the water. They were shocked and angry. Where was the fourth person? Where was Dad?

"Dad!" I screamed. "Dad! Dad!"

I inhaled a mouthful of air, squeezed my lips together, and pulled myself down, afraid of what I would find.

The canoe blocked out the sunlight, and it was dark. Dark and calm. I opened my eyes and saw a body floating. It was vertical, rigid, unmoving. Crying in the water, I kicked over beside it. The body wasn't sinking. It was holding in place. I swam up alongside it and pulled my head above water. There I was, face-to-face with my dad.

He was trapped inside the toppled canoe, holding desperately to the center yolk, his mouth an inch above the water.

"Dad!" I shouted in his face as I urgently grasped something to hold on to. My hands brushed an overturned seat, and I held on greedily, hoping to conserve my little energy. It was dark, cold, and eerie.

I heard a few deep breaths. Then, a calm reply. "I just...need a minute here..."

I inhaled a few deep breaths of my own. "So do I..."

We waited. I thought I heard an owl hoot at that moment. My mind was probably playing tricks on me. It may have been the sound of arguing and yelling coming from the other side of the canoe.

Suddenly, we felt a strong tug on the canoe. It started flipping over. We held on tight.

"Let go!" screamed an unhappy voice.

Dad and I both let go. The canoe pulled over quickly, flipping itself correctly. Dad and I popped out of the water and held on to the canoe's edge. It had a good amount of water in it, but it floated.

Blinking into the sun, I looked at what had pulled the canoe right side up. My brother Johnny, sister Ellie, and three other people with life jackets were there.

The Melfort family.

My dad started to sputter. "Th...th...tha..."

He was trying to say thanks but was in too much shock. His feeble attempts were met with a strong voice.

"What the heck were you doing?" shouted Mr. Melfort. "Never mind! We know what you were up to! Pretending to be hurt or something and then pulling us over!"

"You guys are jerks!" screamed his son Scott. "Our stuff's all wet now too!"

"Let go of our canoe!" said Mrs. Melfort.

"But..." I started.

"Now!"

"Here, Dad," came Josh's voice. He had taken his life jacket off. Lyda was just fine floating on her own. Josh handed it to Dad.

With that, the Melforts grabbed the side of the canoe and started propelling it with kicks over to the makeshift island. Dad and I let go. Within a minute, they were well out of our reach.

We all floated in that spot—my entire family. Finally, my mom spoke up.

"Marc! Are you sure you're okay?" Her voice was shaking.

"I'll just keep this life jacket," he said.

It was the signal to keep going forward. Slowly. But forward nonetheless.

The small island was closer than the shore, so we went there to recover. When we did, the Melforts had already come and gone. They had taken their picture, emptied their canoe of water, and headed back to the main shore. They had unknowingly saved Dad's life. And there was nothing we could do to thank them. Right now, they hated us.

At the island, things were in an uproar. Harlan from Parks Canada was there. He seemed concerned. The Melforts had given him a mouthful.

"There's a family here who says you tried to sabotage them," Harlan said as he held our camera and snapped our picture.

"No!" I interrupted. "We were drowning and..."

"They said you'd try and say that," said Harlan, handing back the camera. "Look, they were agitated. Mumbled something about lodging a complaint. Getting you kicked out of the challenge, getting you kicked out of the country..."

"That's crazy!" said Dad, fire returning to his eyes.

"Just, you'd better head back," said Harlan quietly. "We'll see what happens. You guys okay to get back to shore?"

I looked at Dad. He nodded his head but looked defeated.

"You'd better check out the symbol before you go," said Harlan.

Josh ran over to the backside of the chair and announced, "There's a symbol of a moose here."

We left the red chairs, sealed our camera in the bag, and headed back into the water. Dad was wearing Josh's life jacket. Josh was just fine without it.

We were all too shocked to talk on the swim back. I had a bad feeling about this. Like the end was coming, whether we were ready for it or not.

CHAPTER ELEVEN

LAKE LOUISE

Leaving Lake O'Hara was torturous. Our pace was so slow that it took nearly five hours to return. Once we got in the vehicle, we had to backtrack our drive to Golden, British Columbia to make it to church that Sunday evening. Lyda, Sam, and Rebecca slept through the entire Mass. Lucky. Afterward, Dad stopped by a grocery store and picked up hot dog supplies. He cleaned out the whole store. We went back to our campsite to roast them over a fire.

Things got better. Not just because I felt happy to be alive—nothing can shake *them blues* like a near-death experience. The Melforts were not at the campground. I imagine they'd moved onward to Banff. Probably to avoid us. It made the evening feel more relaxing.

I ate nine hot dogs that night. Josh led the way with an even dozen. Little Sam pounded back five. We were eating real food again and making up for lost time. By real food, I mean processed gray mush from scraps of animal parts swept off the floor, dyed pink, loaded with salt, and then cooked to a black charcoal loaded with carcinogenic nitrates to give that perfect smoky char. Add some sugar mixed with tomato paste on a nutrient-free white bun, and food doesn't get much better.

"Guys!" said my mom with concern. "You can't eat this many hot dogs. It's not healthy."

"Mom," I said, my hand and face a mess of ketchup and charcoal, "kids are starving in Japan."

The following day, we packed up and said goodbye to Yoho National Park. We were on our way to an icon of the Canadian Rockies. Lake Louise.

"Lake Louise. Originally named Emerald Lake by the great railway mountaineer Tom Wilson in 1882. It was changed to avoid confusion with Emerald Lake in Yoho, which Tom Wilson also named after he discovered that lake while hunting for wild horses."

I was giving my usual history lesson that morning as we sped the highway east to Banff National Park.

"That guy sure had a thing for Emerald Lakes," noted Ellie.

"I don't mind that name. But the name later was changed to Lake Louise to honor the daughter of Queen Victoria. The mountain you see at the end of the lake is Mount Victoria. Next to it is Mount Lefroy, where the first recorded mountain climbing death in North America happened. Philip Stanley Abbot, an American lawyer, fell to his death there in 1896. His friends just watched him fall past them and down, smacking his head and body over and over, all the way to the bottom."

"That's enough talk about death," said Dad, wincing a little.

We passed the townsite of Lake Louise and continued onward towards the lake. What would our first impression be of this national treasure, this stunning gem on Earth, this most-photographed natural beauty?

There were cars everywhere. Vehicles as far as the eye could see. There were so many campers, trucks, and buses that it felt like we were parking at a giant football stadium. A sinking feeling came over me. Easy beauty is popular.

It got worse.

"Twenty-one dollars to park!" barked Dad at the electronic parking meter onsite. "Twenty-one dollars to park my vehicle! At a lake in the mountains!"

I started counting up vehicles, desperate to calculate how much money that would make each day. I lost track. Thousands and thousands?

We walked up the busy path. I got a glimpse of the lake, with the mountains in the background. For the hundredth time on that trip, I wondered how so much beauty could exist in one area. The place was downright imperial.

I stared ahead and then nearly walked right into a couple walking back. They glared at me. I saw them start counting how many kids we had, which made me nearly walk into a man in a three-piece suit. He frowned at me. He was counting as well. On the next trip we take, I'll just hold a sign that says *7 Kids*.

I needed help avoiding tourists. Sam had already run into three different people, and Rebecca tripped over two other couples. People everywhere. Not shabby people, either. They were dressed like they mattered. Collared shirts, fancy hats, expensive shoes, and sandals; the people here had class. It all made our large, hopefully down-to-earth, family appear a little—how you say?—out of place.

I thought of how, once in Saskariver, a lady moved in from the big city of Toronto. She had inherited some old family property, so she moved. Shelby Rosthern. A high society kind of woman.

You'd see Shelby, and she'd literally put her nose in the air. She made fun of us for saying *toque* instead of *hat*, *cabin* instead of *cottage*, and, er, *bunnyhug* instead of *hoodie*. Yes, we call hooded sweaters bunnyhugs where I live. Not that Ms. Rosthern would wear a bunnyhug. "Too hick," she'd say. What I'm getting at is she looked down on us because we were different. I think we in turn made fun of her. We'd laugh about how she couldn't handle the cold, that she couldn't make a pie properly, that she pronounced apricot like *ay*-pricot.

So, there we were at Lake Louise. A large family dressed in smelly and ripped clothing wandering around and bumping into people. Being stared at in the process. Were they looking down on us? Or were we being like Ms. Rosthern and looking down on them? Maybe it's the fault of both sides? I think we all like to look down on those different from us.

Whatever it was, it was something. I looked at the Lake Louise Chateau, and I saw two people on the front lawn being served lobster by a waiter dressed in a tuxedo. I saw half a dozen sports cars, altogether worth enough money to buy my entire town of Saskariver. And the brides! Brides everywhere. It's a place to get wedding pictures. Not me, though. I'm not getting married. Eww.

There was a lot of extra noise at Lake Louise this morning. A ceaseless roar of engines and power meant only one thing: a new money-making red chair gimmick to endure.

"Another one!" said Josh, pointing to the sky.

"They're all black and yellow," I said. "All that same BMF company."

"That's the same company with the hot air balloons and everything else," added Ellie. "They must be rich!"

Rich, like everyone else at Lake Louise. Or at least as people pretended to be.

It wasn't hard to find out the day's mission. Rent a helicopter for $400 per person and ride to the red chairs. Or, if one was not inclined to shell out the money, hike eleven kilometers and nearly eight hundred meters up—that's seven miles and twenty-five hundred feet for people like my dad—to a place called the Big Beehive.

I stretched my legs—time to get to work.

The hike lingered around a good chunk of Lake Louise to start. Miraculously, the farther we went, the fewer people there were. By the time we were climbing up the trail, almost no one was there. Waterfalls, old forests, and excellent views led the way. I was starting to like Lake Louise. Then the switchbacks came. Up and up. The kind that makes your legs scream in agony. I was starting to curse Lake Louise.

We got to the top. Thankfully, the helicopter spot was a little way from the red chairs, so it wasn't too loud. I'm not sure how the helicopter riders managed to walk a few extra steps without fainting from exhaustion.

We took our picture and checked out the secret symbol. It was bizarre. Like those old-time scales people would use to balance or measure out things like gold. A balance of some sort. Bizarre indeed.

My family was finishing a trail snack when Kelly approached us. Kelly is my least favorite park staff member. She looked serious today.

"Well, now, the Storthoaks family is here," she began. "I was hoping to see you. We've been tracking you guys."

"What do you mean tracking us?" asked Dad, his nose twitching in surprise.

"Oh, nothing," she said.

"Where's Harlan today?" I asked. I was genuinely wondering. I didn't expect her answer.

"Not here," she snapped. Kelly flung her blonde hair back like a spoiled five-year-old who doesn't get her way. "There's a good group of staff here today helping out. Real *team* players, you know. Don't think about...him."

"So why are you happy to see us?" asked my mom.

"I said *hoping*, not *happy*," said Kelly, still upset. "I'm here to warn you. We've received an official complaint that we're investigating." Her lips curled into a smile.

"Who complained? And for what?" asked Dad.

"An honest and responsible family has complained about an incident yesterday at Lake O'Hara. You are under investigation for many things; that's all I will say for now."

"The Melforts!" I shouted.

"Where are they?" said Mom. "We can figure this out."

"We saw you were coming here today," Kelly said, rolling her eyes, "so we advised this family of victims to go to the other red chair location to avoid being emotionally disturbed."

"Emotionally disturbed!" exploded Dad. "I'll bet they are!"

"Exactly what I'm saying," said Kelly, her face snarling again. "Now I feel like you're threatening me too. No, don't argue, I feel it, and that's what matters." She took a few breaths. This was getting weird.

"I mean," said Dad, "we would like to know what this investigation is really about. We've done no wrong!"

Kelly interrupted Dad. "We're investigating. That's all I will say right now. We might be in contact with you shortly. Don't worry about finding us. We'll find you when the time comes. If you'll excuse me, I have responsible, *paying* families to help get the best of their red chair experience."

She turned and left. We picked our jaws up from the ground and made our own exit. Down the Big Beehive. Past the lake. Dodging swarms of tourists. And to the vehicle.

"Paying families," said Dad as we got ready to leave. "I paid twenty-one bucks just to park here today. Twenty-one!" He started shouting to be heard over the tour helicopter roaring overhead. "If that's not paying, I don't know what is!"

As we drove east to the campground near the town of Banff, I read through my book that Father Wally gave me, motion sickness or not. I was trying to take my mind off what was happening. This Family Red Chair Challenge was getting strange. Strange and uncomfortable. I felt like giving up. Like calling it quits. I'm sure the rest of my family did as well. *A large family is not without honor except in its hometown*, I thought, misquoting the Good Book.

I flipped to the front of my *Rocky Mountain Stories*.

Joey. You will be needed by others. Be ready for this. You will be needed.
I pray you grow up.

God Bless always,
Fr. Wally Zsxyltchovskiwehveltskibetishly
(Psalm 12-1).

Strange and uncomfortable indeed.

We pulled into Tunnel Mountain Campground by Banff. We were nearing the end of the adventure.

The question was, were we going to finish our adventure?

Chapter Twelve

Banff's Sulphur Mountain

W e sat around the fire that night. We should've been scared and unsettled. The opposite was true. It was as if everything we'd been through together as a family had brought us closer. What was another challenge? Besides, we were close to winning. We had six out of seven secret symbols. Soon, it would be time to piece them all together.

The sun was still up. However, the evening chill was starting to pierce our skin. The fire was warm, the pine trees sheltered us from the wind, and we sat around joking and remembering.

"Remember at Yoho Lake how Mom started washing our jackets in the lake like it was laundry day or something?" I chuckled.

"And I didn't get your help either," Mom replied. "Just like laundry day."

"Yeah, but at least she didn't walk into the wrong washroom," said Josh. "Joey had his head down at the Lake Louise Chateau when we stopped in. Stepped right into the women's washroom. I bet those fancy ladies were ready to throw high heels at you."

My siblings laughed as I tried to explain that Josh had shoved me in there.

"Well, Josh was sneaking around and getting in all those wedding pictures at Lake Louise," I said. "One of the brides saw him once and turned around to smack him. Josh started running away. A new bride in her long, perfect white dress, chasing my stupid brother half around the lake. With people taking thousands of pictures of it all."

"Stupid brother?" said Dad. "What about the stupid groom? He just stood there, then bent down and shined his shoes while waiting."

"A real knight in shining armor," said Mom.

"Or shining shoes," I corrected.

"Remember how the cashier at the grocery store in Golden asked where the party was when she saw all those hot dogs we were buying?" said Ellie.

"I think she was serious!" I said.

"That she thought we were throwing a party?" laughed Dad. "Or she was asking to join the party?"

"What about that time Joey ate the granola bar that the Melforts chucked at us?" said Johnny.

"He never lets food go to waste," said Josh, pinching my stomach.

"Whatever, at least the Melforts aren't here," I said. "Probably Kelly had to take them to a safe space to recover from the emotional trauma."

"You have that effect on people," said Josh.

We laughed and chuckled until very late, which for us was about 8:00 p.m. We're not exactly party animals, you might say. When you climb mountains, however, you need your beauty sleep.

The following day was exciting. It started to sink in that we were near the end of our seven-chair challenge. With one more clue, we could start piecing together where the grand finale would be. Just one more mountain!

Where was that? The famous Sulphur Mountain near the historic Banff Springs Hotel. I think the idea was for Family Red Chair Challenge participants to get an expensive room at the hotel. I had to hand it to the organizers of the challenge: they sure knew how to squeeze every last dollar out of people.

We pulled into the parking lot for Sulphur Mountain. The challenge was easily predictable—either pay to take the gondola up, or climb the mountain.

"Joey?" said Dad.

"Sulphur Mountain," I said. "Named in 1916 for the hot springs on its lower slopes. The hike is eleven kilometers total and seven hundred and fifty-nine meters up."

"Joey?" repeated Dad.

"Nearly seven miles and almost twenty-five hundred feet of elevation," I said.

"Thank you."

By now, we had what you would call *mountain legs*. We had endurance, strength, and speed on our side. Saving money had a physical payoff. Scott Melfort could work out all morning, and it wouldn't come close to what we had. Why am I mentioning him again? Ugh.

The trail was in great shape. There wasn't anything too technical to overcome. Nor were there great views on the way. Just steep and steady climbing. It only took us two and a half hours to trek to the top. From there, we planned to get our picture, check out the view while having lunch, and then head off.

That was the plan. But the challenge had a plot twist. In other words, we couldn't find the red chairs. Not anywhere. There were regular tourists everywhere, but not many families milling around. Where were they? Dad said we should go inside the main interpretive center to find out.

We walked inside. Then we groaned. This wasn't good.

It turns out that Sulphur Mountain has four peaks. The red chairs were all the way at the fourth peak. To get there involved real-deal mountain climbing. Like mountain climbing for experts. Lest you end up as poor Philip Stanley Abbott at Mount Lefroy in 1896. Tumbling down like a rag doll. Not pleasant.

"So," stammered Mom, "how are families supposed to get to the red chairs from here? Are they trying to kill us? Is that what this is about?" Her voice was escalating.

"No, not exactly," said Dad. "Just kill our wallets. Look over there. By the big windows. That's a rental place."

"What do you rent?" I asked. "Red chairs?"

"I wish," said Dad. "You rent mountain guides. I mean, you pay for someone to guide you along the mountain's ridge. And you pay to use all the safety equipment, helmets, and harnesses. I'll bet you pay per person. Hundreds of dollars per person."

"I don't like this," said Mom.

"Well, is this it?" I shouted. "We're done? After getting to six chairs!"

"It would be in the thousands of dollars, Joey," said Dad. I could see he was shocked and disappointed.

I stormed outside the interpretive center and walked down the path for a minute. The sky was clear, and the view was stunning. Banff was something. Imagine building a town in the most outstanding place you could find in the Rockies. The founding of the town of Banff was something like that. What did it matter? I'd always remember Banff as the place where my dreams were shattered.

I must've been grimacing as I stood looking down on the town because an older couple strolling past stopped to say something.

"You groovy?" asked the man. He had a massive head of gray dreadlocks, a tie-dye shirt, and baggy orange shorts. I'd say he was a hippy if I didn't know any better—an honest-to-goodness hippy. I'd never seen one before in Saskariver.

"I'm good," I lied.

"Forest," said an old lady in a hemp hat, long white dress, and rainbow necklace, "I think he's just chilling."

The man, apparently named Forest, nodded. "Got it, Chick."

"I'm just frustrated," I said. Of all the people to open up to... An old hippy couple at the top of a mountain! "We have one last red chair to get. One more! And it's way over on the last ridge. We can't afford to hire someone to take us there."

"Just like the government, man," said Forest. "Gotta crush the little dude."

"Something like that," I said before adding a "dude."

"You know, young wilderness man, life is like a journey," said Chick. "It's not about the destination. It's all the journey. And our journey should be love."

I didn't know what she was saying. Isn't life a journey *to* a destination?

"There's a saying I really dig," interrupted Forest. "There is freedom waiting for you in the breezes of the sky, and you ask, 'What if I fall?' Oh, but my darling, 'What if you fly?'"

"You mean I can fly to those red chairs?" I asked.

"You can do whatever your heart sets itself on," said Chick, showing her yellow teeth, or what was left of them, as she smiled.

"Uh, I need to go find my parents," I said.

"Look, son," said Forest. "Chill. I've been high up here many times, er, and I know how to fly to the fourth peak. Everyone goes on the top ridge or to the left of it. Nah. Dip a little below the ridge. On the right side. Just like, bypass the other summits. They'll distract you, man. Oh, and there's one psychedelic section. It's bad, dude. You got a ladder to success, though! Then you're like there. Copacetic?"

"I don't take things from strangers," I said.

"No, little dude!" laughed Forest. "Like, sound good?"

"Yeah, I think so."

"Then go fly!" said Chick. "Fly, little white dove, fly!"

"Maybe I will," I said, gathering my strength. "Maybe I will!"

I walked back to the interpretive center. How was I sup-posed to explain this to my parents? I decided to try something unusual. Something risky. Something unexpected. I was going to tell them the truth.

"Mom! Dad!" I shouted when I saw them standing inside the building. "I just met some old hippies! They said to go a little down from the ridge and to the right. Ignore the other summits, they said. And not to wonder about falling, but flying..." This was not panning out so well. "Like, flying like a white dove. Up high. We, er, can do it if it's a journey of love, er, and not a destiny. Our ladder of success..."

"Joey, are you okay?" asked Mom, concerned.

I couldn't answer.

"I think he's trying to say that there is a better way to get to the fourth peak if we go to the right and a little down from the ridge and bypass the other peaks. Right?" said Dad.

"Copa...stetic? Copacetic?" I said.

Dad looked at Mom. She nodded. I smiled.

"Let's at least check it out," said Dad. "We'll go slow and safe. No falling."

"Only flying, dude," I said.

Chapter Thirteen

The Fourth Peak

We decided to climb alongside a mountain. Much of the path was forest-enclosed. The only real danger was tripping on a root. This got our hopes up. Maybe this wasn't so bad after all.

Soon, the trees started thinning out. We walked on a two-foot-wide path low and to the right of the main ridge. It still wasn't a steep drop-off on the right. It would be bad if we fell, but not the end of the world. My only concern was that we were high up, and I could see everything below. The view was distracting, like it was calling for me to look, slip, and tumble.

We could hear chatter and noise coming from the other side of the mountain. I imagine there were ziplines and harnesses out there and that the "mountain climbing" to the fourth peak was really a makeshift roller coaster ride. That's how things were done, all courtesy of that BMF company. They must be billionaires.

The path got rocky. We slowed down and took careful steps. The younger kids held the hands of either a parent or an older sibling. The lack of wind made it possible. So we continued on our way, not looking back. Not thinking of falling, but only of flying, dude.

Before long, the path became not a path. It became a narrow ledge with a steep drop-off. It became too treacherous.

"Dad," I said, "I think we need to go back a bit and down. That's what Forest said."

"The forest is talking to you?" said Josh.

"He means the hippy," said Dad. "Well, we'll try it for a bit."

Backtrack, and downward we went. There seemed to be a little path through the trees. Not an official path. Rather, like a path made in secret. A secret path. Forged by the work of hippy fairies.

The secret path took us around summits two and three. However, we were going downward as we went around. The peak was up, and we were heading down. I guess you can't trust hippies after all.

"This better trend upwards soon," said Dad, looking concerned. "We might be finished if it doesn't."

"You've messed us up, Joey!" complained Josh.

"No! Trust me," I said.

"You have no friends at home," Josh persisted, "and then you make some friends with old hippies." He wasn't feeling it. He couldn't fly.

It hurt. It wasn't far from the truth, either.

"The bush is ending. I think I see a path ahead," said Dad. "But..."

He didn't need to finish. There was a short, doable path that led upwards to the fourth peak. The only thing in the way was a gap in the rocks. A four-foot-long gap that dropped down a thousand or more feet below. We were stuck.

"Forest must be a little unwell today. He thinks we can fly," said Josh.

"There must be a way!" I nearly screamed. "I'll bet there is."

"It's okay, Joey," said Mom. "You didn't know. We're stuck, and it's not your fault."

I looked around at the rest of my family. They had their heads down. I'm unsure if they were just disappointed that this was the end or that I had led them to this place. I walked back to the trees. Honestly, I wanted to cry a bit. I know, I shouldn't admit that. But I'm not a robot or a machine. I trust people—very few people—and it hurts extra fierce when I get let down. Maybe it's why I'm a misfit. I can't pick out what is normal and acceptable, what is a stupid risk, or who is untrustworthy.

A few tears fell. I leaned against a tree and closed my eyes. I was tired. I gave it all but had nothing left to give. Father Wally was wrong. I wasn't going to be needed by anyone.

The tree I was leaning on had two short branches sticking out above my head that seemed weird, like they didn't belong. I reached up and poked at them, and they gave way. I spun my head around to the other side of the tree and saw what these branches were. They were the top-side rails of a makeshift ladder.

I reached over and pulled the ladder down. It was fashioned out of a spruce tree, fastened together with hemp rope, a good twelve feet tall and three feet wide, and definitely homemade. There were far too many rungs on it—one rung every four to six inches. Instantly, I understood. This was no simple ladder. This was Forest's trick.

"Guys!" I shouted. "I know how to get past the gap! We use this ladder." I hauled it out for all to see.

Their faces dropped. Not in a good way, either.

"You're nuts!" cried Ellie.

"No, I'm not," I said, dragging it over to the gap before being told not to. I laid it flat, and it fit perfectly. It was a perfect little bridge connecting one side to the other. What's a thousand-foot drop in between got to do with it?

"Time to fly," I cried as I started crawling across.

I think my parents were screaming at me, maybe, I don't know. I was too intent on crossing to notice. Given any other circumstance, crossing four feet on this three-foot-wide ladder would've been nothing. A walk in the park. A Sunday stroll. This was a little different.

I made it to the end and turned to face my consequences. My parents' eyes were bulging from their sockets. They didn't notice Josh hop on the ladder and follow my lead.

"Hey, what?" said Dad.

Next came Johnny. Then Ellie. When Rebecca started, we formed a human chain to help her across. It was short, quick, and, if you didn't stop to think about it, not too terrifying. Sam came over using the same help we gave Rebecca. Finally, there were my parents and the baby to consider. Mom blubbered her way across, inching slowly along the makeshift bridge and down. Dad was next. With Lyda strapped securely on his back, he moved forward.

In a split second, there was a crack. The ladder wasn't meant for such weight. Dad practically jumped over with Lyda as an even louder crack was heard.

"Yikes!" he shouted.

"Dad!" I replied.

"We did it!" screamed Josh.

"I'm going to kill you!" said Mom, breathing heavily.

"We're...good," said Dad, huffing and puffing. "I'm sure it's nothing that an old hippy couldn't do."

We pulled the ladder over to our side. It wasn't broken after all. The sound was louder than any actual damage.

"Let's keep going," I said, not wanting to linger. Lingering meant talking. Talking meant blaming me for not being safe. Blaming me meant being distracted from the task at hand. We had red chairs to find.

The path went up sharply but never in a manner that was too dangerous. Within ten minutes, we were pulling our noses above the ridge and to the final summit. What a sight!

Two red chairs were there. Many families with crazy hiking gear strapped around their bodies laughed and chatted. It was like I thought: their "treacherous mountain climbing" was basically a zipline from one peak to another. Scary, to be sure, but safe. Far safer than what we'd done.

We went to the red chairs and had a picture. I looked at the last secret symbol. This was exciting. Now, we could piece the puzzle together.

"A swing set?" I said.

"Looks like a slide behind it, too," said Johnny.

"A park?" said Mom.

"Maybe," came a familiar voice.

"Harlan!" I said. "Good to see you!"

"You did it," said Harlan. "You made it through." Though he was smiling, he looked afraid. His short gray hair had hints of sweat, and he rubbed his forehead repeatedly. All of which is to say, he looked nervous.

"We made it through," said Dad. "How are things?"

"Oh, you know," said Harlan as a family walked past, "glad to be in Banff! Yes! Great times here! Love this Family Red Chair Challenge! Golly, thanks!"

When the family was out of sight, Harlan whispered, "I need to talk with you guys right now."

We made our way off the main summit to a little nook surrounded by trees. Harlan held his hand up for us to be quiet while he listened intently. His eyes scanned in every direction. This was getting to be too much. And people say old hippies act weird.

Satisfied that all was clear, Harlan whispered, "They've finished their investigation."

"Who are *they*?" asked Mom with a bit too much volume.

"Shh!" said Harlan, reminding me of Miss Fancy Spudd whenever I cleared my throat at the library. "*They* are the powers-that-be in the National Park office. Along with the police. Basically, some high-up government officials. I mean..."

"Why should these powers-that-be care about us?" I asked.

"Because..." he began, unsure how much to reveal. "Because. Okay? They've decided several things. It has to do with the Melforts...and other things."

"What about these other things?" I interrupted again.

"Listen," said Harlan. Listening wasn't my strong point when flustered. "They're coming to get you. Tomorrow around eight in the morning. They'll take you out for questioning, or worse. I don't know what it will lead to. At the very least, they'll delay you enough so you don't win the Family Red Chair Challenge."

We were stunned. Was Harlan making any sense? Was *any of this* making any sense? Ziplines and roller coasters and helicopters as part of some family challenge? Endless money changing hands? Official investigations against a lowly family from the prairies?

"This doesn't feel like what a trip to the Rocky Mountains should be," I said.

Harlan's eyes rolled in the back of his mind. He was flipping through memories in his brain. Happier times. Peaceful times.

"It's not," he began. "It never was. We used to have a great team in all the Rocky Mountain parks. Families came and enjoyed nature. It was what it should be. But a couple of years ago it was announced to us to prepare for this challenge. To start planning for a summer extravaganza. They said there'd be future ones, too. Some company was hired to set it all up. It became this massive money-maker. Where the money's gone, I couldn't say. Not to servicing the national parks, I can tell you that."

"Oh Harlan, I'm so sorry for you," said Mom.

"Don't be sorry for me," said Harlan. "Several people on my staff quit in protest. I should've, too. I... I was too scared to quit. I convinced myself I'd do more good staying on. They brought in new staff. Brainwashed people. Some of them, anyway. Others were simply brain-dead."

"Like Kelly!" I added.

"I've been going along with it," said Harlan. "I sold out. To keep my job here. I've betrayed the playful pikas and innocent marmots, the majestic moose and the mournful mountain goats..."

"Well then," said Dad, finding Harlan's monologue ending to be awkward, "we need to get out of here. What do you suggest?"

"Finish the challenge as soon as you can. See what happens. But you need to figure out where to go by eight in the morning."

"Can't you just tell us where?" Mom asked.

"I don't even know where it is," said Harlan. "I'm not what you'd call *in-the-know* on staff. Just finish it if you can."

"Is there a way we can leave here safely?" asked Mom.

Harlan looked at her, looked at me, looked at all of us, then smiled.

"Leave it to me," he said.

We had the complete VIP treatment. Harlan suited us all up with complimentary equipment, and we sailed the motorized zipline much of the way back. Sailing across the sky was terrifying. My mind went wild. I think my heart stopped beating. I loved it. Afterward, to complete the way back, Harlan took us on a guided "mountain climbing" adventure with safety nets, temporary bridges, and a stair system.

If that wasn't enough, Harlan snuck us onto the gondolas. He said not to worry about him. If he got fired, oh well. He said he'd be happy going on with life, knowing he did the right thing. So, we had a free ride down; from there, we raced to our vehicle, through downtown Banff, and back to our campsite. We had some figuring out to do. And we had to do it right away.

We needed to fly, dude.

CHAPTER FOURTEEN

THE SECRET SYMBOLS

Before I started homeschooling, I went to school. Real school. I wasn't the most popular kid there. I wasn't hated either. For the most part, I was just there.

I had this one teacher, Mr. Gordon. He had a thick British accent, which brought severity to everything he said. Like every lesson was life and death. To be asked four times four felt like you were handcuffed and locked inside a police interrogation room, being questioned about *where the money went* while a hostile detective tapped the table with a billy club in a disturbing rhythm.

Mr. Gordon was a smoker. Every hour, on the hour, he'd take a break from being grumpy and say, "I need to de-chalk the chalk off my hands!" He'd be giddy as he said it. Sometimes, he hadn't touched a piece of chalk all day.

Mr. Gordon would sneak away to the school's basement, the boiler room they called it, and inhale a cigarette or two. Our class was left alone while he did this. If you wanted to get revenge on a kid, you'd say to Mr. Gordon when he returned: "Teacher, Robert said he needs help with his math!" Then, Mr. Gordon would go over to Robert. Robert would wince in discomfort, and his face would turn yellowish green. Mr. Gordon smelled like a skunk who bathed in rancid cabbage after each cigarette. It was disgusting. And yet, to this day, I know I'll never take up smoking. I can still smell *that*.

One day, Mr. Gordon left for his smoke break, and the bigshot personalities in class turned their attention to me. A boy named Clay especially was after me to prove myself somehow. Clay wanted to be entertained, I wanted to be left alone, and something had to be done to let us both have our peace.

"Go see where Mr. Gordon has gone," said Clay, thinking I was an easy target to bully.

"Oh, he'd never do that!" said a few girls, giggling.

Without saying anything, I was gone. Two minutes later, I returned.

"What happened?" asked Clay, eyes wide in anticipation.

"I followed him downstairs. When he got to the boiler room, he turned his head to see if he was being followed. I ducked behind a garbage can. He went in. I trailed right behind."

"Did you get caught?"

"How?" I continued, "I saw him smoking. He turned green. Then red with anger. Said he'd call my parents and everything. I told him I'd tell the principal about his smoking if he did that. He turned green again. He calmed down and basically begged me not to say anything. I told him I'd think about it. I'll bet I will have some great marks the rest of the year."

With that, Clay and the rest of the class had a secret respect for me. I did something cool, something they would never dare, and came out on top.

I never told them that I made up that story. I never went down to the boiler room. I went to the washroom and came back. But I knew the class would be easily impressed, and they'd leave me alone. It was a win-win.

Why bring this up? What does this have to do with finding secret codes?

I bring up random facts because that's what I do. And because this random story, if I may pump my own tires for a minute, hints that I think about things differently. Sometimes, I don't know where my brain is taking me other than a place far from others. I remember random facts about turtles while forgetting where I am or what day it is. I've been called a misfit. I think I'm just a little shy. That and I like creating in my head. Creating and connecting in my own way. This has advantages, especially when it comes to the life-and-death Family Red Chair Challenges.

We sat by the fire at our campsite. One of our logs was burning a little funny, and the smell was a little off, which reminded me of Mr. Gordon. I smiled. Good times.

"I've been thinking about these codes all day," said Dad, burning another marshmallow. He was in triple digits for burning those sugar puffballs this trip.

"They don't make sense," said Josh. "A *key, mountains, toes* or *foot, rock* or *diamond, moose,* a *balance* or *scale,* and a *playset* or a *park*…"

"The *key* to finding the *mountain* adventure is to *walk* over *rocks* to where the *moose* is and *scale* a *playset,*" said Ellie. "How's that?"

"That literally makes no sense," said Josh.

"Let's see you do better!" she challenged.

Josh paused momentarily. "The *key* to these *mountains* is *walking* to the *diamonds,* where the *moose* can *balance* and *play.*"

"We're not getting anywhere, are we?" said Dad, stating the obvious.

"Joey," said Mom, "you haven't said a single word this whole time."

The smoke was in my face again. I was a smoke magnet. I moved to another spot around the fire.

"Stop that!" said Ellie. "You're bringing the smoke over here."

Sure enough, it followed me. I went to another place next to Josh and Johnny. They picked up their camping chairs and scattered to a different location. We rearranged our spot around the fire several times.

"That's interesting," I said.

"What?" said Ellie.

"*We* started in Jasper, but did the contest rules say that's where the actual starting point is?"

"Well, yes!" said Dad. "At least, I assume it did."

"Assume," I said, "let's not get into what that means. Did it say where to start?"

Dad went to the vehicle and pulled the printed rules from the glove compartment. Finally, he shook his head and said there was nothing about it.

"So, let's rearrange them. *Keys. Mountains. Foot* or *Toes. Rock* or *Diamond. Moose. Balance* or *Scale. Playset* or *Park.*"

"How about: the *foot* of the *mountains* by the *moose park* is where you will find *diamonds* to *balance* and..." rambled Josh.

"How about no?" said Dad.

"The first part is pretty simple," I piped up. "I think that one symbol was a rock, not a diamond. If you do that, then it flows. *Rock. Key. Mountains. Park.*"

"A Rocky Mountains park!" shouted Ellie.

"That's obvious," said Josh.

"It wasn't ten seconds ago," said Dad.

"We'll see," I said.

"What next?" asked Mom.

"I think *moose* is important," said Dad. "But I'm not sure how to narrow it down."

"I was thinking about that," I added. "There are so many moose, and moose names, in the Canadian Rockies. Moose Lakes, Moose Rivers, Moose Streams, Moose Mountains. Moose Hotels. We'd never be able to check out all these places in time."

"So, do we just pick one?" asked Ellie.

"No, we need to figure it out," insisted Dad. "What about those toes? I think the symbol was closer to toes than a foot."

"A place where people stub their toes?" suggested Josh.

"You mean like everywhere in the world?" I said. "No. The toes and balance scale are so out of place in this. I wonder if they belong together."

"Like toes give your feet balance?" said Johnny.

"True," said Dad. "I'm not sure how that helps with a location."

We were stumped. I needed to think, but there was too much chatter. I needed silence. To get into my own mind. To create. I stepped away from the fire.

"I'll be back in a minute," I said.

"Dad, are we going to win?" asked Sam. Clearly, his brain was in the right frame of mind.

Dad was confident. "Yes, we will, son."

I stepped out onto a back path behind the campsite. Pine trees and fresh-scented moss surrounded me. Walking helps me think. It activates the brain. And yes, my toes help me balance. Whatever that means. I'd climbed enough mountains to know that. I'd stubbed my toes a few times, too. Like on Whistlers Mountain. But if it were any different, I'd end up almost like that one guy from the story I'd read. How would that help me win? We will win. *Yes, we will, son…* Toes to balance. *We will, son…* Walking back to my family now. *Will, son…*

"Guys!" I shouted, running back to camp. "I've got it!"

"What?" said Mom.

"Is it contagious?" said Dad.

"It's Wilson! I've cracked the code!" I persisted. "It's part of a history story. I read it in my book Father Wally gave me!"

"Not the guy who fell to his death again," said Ellie.

"No," I spoke rapidly, "the Tom Wilson Christmas story! Remember, he snowshoed over a hundred kilometers, or like seventy miles, to get home for Christmas. He went through blizzards and everything. When he finished, so were several of his toes. They froze. A doctor cut off toe parts to help save his feet. Tom was happy with the job the doctor did. He said the doctor cut just the perfect amount of toe from each foot. He said it *balanced* out perfectly."

"And?" asked Dad. "Are we supposed to go all over the place like him?"

"Yes!" I said. "And no! We can narrow it down. Tom Wilson set out along the Pipestone Pass to get to Banff that Christmas."

"So it's in Banff?" Josh interrupted. "Are you sure?"

"It *is* in Banff, and it *isn't* in Banff," I said. "Banff was the first national park, made in 1885. But it was originally named Rocky Mountains Park. And from there, we get to Pipestone Pass, which leads to Banff, but it's in the backcountry."

"What about the moose?" said Mom.

"Look it up on a map," I explained.

Dad went back to the vehicle and pulled out several maps. Thankfully, he was a map-o-holic.

"Moose Meadows. Moose Hotel. Moose Lake." He was reading all the things that said *moose* in it.

"Find Bow Lake and then look to the right, past the highway," I said. "I think Pipestone Pass is right of Helen Lake or Mosquito Mountain. Something like that."

"Moose, moose, moose..." my dad mumbled. "Moose... Moose! Moose Lake! Right near the Pipestone Pass area!"

We all cheered! We knew where to go now.

"Wait!" commanded Dad. "Hold on! How on earth do we get there? There's no road. No nothing. Just mountains in the way."

"Then we go over the mountains," I said. "We walk."

"Walk to Moose Lake?" said Mom. "How long would that take?"

"The question is," said Dad, "how many days would that take?"

"And?" asked Mom.

"The answer is, we'd better go pick up a few groceries and supplies tonight. We're going backpacking tomorrow." Dad turned and looked at me, then added, "We have a challenge to win."

"Dad, we're going to win?" asked Sam again.

"Yes, we will, son."

CHAPTER FIFTEEN

MOOSE LAKE?

We started packing up our tent before sunlight. Four-thirty in the morning. There was no time for breakfast, morning coffee, or even waking up properly. It was up and out before six. To try and fool people, Dad left a note behind. It was a fake trip itinerary. The note mentioned all our stops, the distance between each, and then had an arrow pointing to our next stop. It had all the codes written on it, then said, "Moose Lake Loop, Jasper." It was worth a try.

We were driving west and then north onto the Icefield Parkway. Mom passed out granola bars as we sped along. I was too tired to eat, but I shoved it in my mouth anyway. I was too tired to even think about the kids in Japan. Lyda cried for the first half of the trip. If you've never experienced a baby crying for an extended period, it's like having all your senses violently shaken. You can't think. Then you start to get dizzy. By the end, you want to cry alongside the baby.

As the sun was popping up, Dad pulled into a small parking lot on the left side of the highway. It was someplace called Mosquito Creek. And no, we didn't see a single mosquito that morning. He pulled the vehicle into a spot past the parking lot and out of the highway's sight, surrounded by trees and brush. It was worth a shot.

"Let's get loaded up," Dad called.

I soon realized this was no ordinary hike. It was Mom who strapped Lyda on her back. Dad took a backpack loaded with our tent, cooking supplies, and a ton of food. The rest of us kids, from Josh down to Sam, had our backpacks stuffed with as much as we could carry. It was showtime.

"Okay, quick!" shouted Dad when there was a lull in traffic. "Follow me!"

Thanks to our heavy loads, we crossed the highway in a run that looked more like a waddle. I swear I could smell horse manure as we crossed. Like there was a nearby stable. I didn't have time to ask anyone else about it. The trailhead was ahead, and we had to sneak onto it. This trail wasn't like those extensive wide trails we used on our other hikes. This was a backcountry trail. It was more rugged, demanding, and solitary. I liked it.

You'll never guess what came next. We had to climb up. Steeply. Without mercy. The trail was like a mean gym teacher who makes you run laps the entire class. But the gym class ended, so to speak, and our ascent became more gradual. Thank goodness. Carrying a heavy pack is not something I was prepared for.

We reached the Mosquito Creek Backcountry Campground over three hours later. We were pooped. Don't snicker! We were! There was one lonely tent set up. This made Dad nervous, so he had us climb through bush around the campground to where the trail continued.

From there, the path degraded into a mess of roots, mud, and more roots. Oh, and it rose steeply again.

I was getting tired. An eleven-year-old boy can't complain when the going gets tough. An eleven-year-old boy must work hard and show no weakness. An eleven-year-old boy may not understand why—as I didn't understand that day—and must be at peace with not knowing why. It's all in the long process of one day becoming a man.

My four-year-old brother, on the other hand, sure did complain. At one point, he flopped on the ground, crying and kicking. Mom and Dad were gentle with him. I was ready to leave him behind. I thought he wanted to win?

All evil must pass—every night breaks. Even dragon-like mountains have their end. We broke through to some meadows. Oh those glorious meadows, walled in by breathtaking mountains, towering peaks, and occasional waterfalls and fresh streams. We were getting somewhere. The question was, where?

"Dad, where are we?" I asked.

"Grizzly bear country," he replied. "Just keep making noise."

I did. We all did. A large family, when it sticks together, has *that* at least going for them. The ability to make noise. Effortlessly.

As the day wore on, our bodies wore out. Dad kept encouraging us: "Just a little bit farther." These words soon became a running joke.

"How far to Kazakhstan?" Josh would ask.

"Just a little bit farther," we'd all reply.

"How far to the moon?" I'd ask.

"Just a little bit farther," was the response.

"How much more until we all pass out and die?" asked Johnny.

"Just a little bit farther."

Just a little bit farther did come, and we were at a campground called Fish Lakes. By campground, I mean a small portion of a field and trees designated for camping. It was deserted, so Dad had us stop. To be safe, however, we explored a little and found a place to set up camp away from the main camping area.

"Tent up," he said. "We cook away from our campsite. No food in your packs. All food gets hung from a tree when we're done. And don't go anywhere alone!"

That night around the fire, we discussed our strategy. The plan was to make it to Moose Lake tomorrow afternoon. We'd take a route from a high ridge, which made for an open view of where we were going but also exposed us to the elements more. With any luck, we could finish this challenge tomorrow. Maybe even as champions. Probably as champions. No one else was around, which meant we were in first place. Right?

"How are people supposed to get to this place?" I asked. "Helicopters again?"

"I was thinking of that," said Dad. "There was a smell of horses this morning. I think they quietly have stables set up and a different path for horses to carry people to the place. I mean, that assumes we're in the right place."

The thought of being in the wrong place didn't sit well with me. Nor the idea of being eaten by a grizzly bear. I didn't sleep well.

The following day, we ate more granola bars, used the pit toilet for, ahem, certain duties, packed up camp, and looked for our trail. After some exploring, we found a makeshift trail downward from the pit toilet and across a stream. We headed north, almost straight upward, towards the ridge that would take us to Moose Lake.

The views were spectacular, until the rain came, that is. At first, it was a drizzle, just enough to make us miserable, then it was a downpour, which forced us to descend and take shelter. For two hours, we waited. When the rain lessened, we set out. The trail was muddy and slippery. But we were close. Just a little bit farther, as Dad kept saying. Finally, *The Moment* came.

"Dad! I see something!" I shouted, pointing below and off to the right.

In the distance, as far as could be seen in the weather conditions, a small tent or structure was in place. It was near a lake. Moose Lake! I couldn't see red chairs yet, but I knew we were in the right spot.

"Stop running!" said Dad. "We're still on a slippery path and high up. *And* we need to stick together. Slow and steady... Just a little bit farther."

We started the long, careful descent towards the lake. Everything was soaked. I assumed we'd be getting blisters soon. What did it matter? We were going to win!

By now, the trail went straight north to the lake. It was hard to see because of our drop in elevation. I looked behind from where we'd come. What a trek! I looked to the right side of our trail, where another set of mountains stood. I could see a tall waterfall. The water was roaring down from all the rain. It was mesmerizing—so much water.

Then it hit me. There was something at the top of the waterfall, almost hanging from its edge. But what? A log? An animal? It made no sense. My skin tingled in alarm.

"Um…" I began. "I think there's something up there at the waterfall."

My family stopped to look.

"I don't see anything," said Mom.

A "me neither" chorus followed from everyone else.

"Joey," said Dad. "We need to focus. The end is in sight. Let's look ahead."

We walked onward. I didn't feel so good. A tightening in my belly. A pressure on my forehead. Just look ahead.

I would never suggest disobeying your parents. It never ends well. The only time it works is if you have *that* feeling. I think they call it conscience. When you know you need to do something, and it is the right thing to do, you feel bad until you do it.

I slipped to the right, away from my family. Stealthily, without being noticed. I started trotting closer to the waterfall. I planned to get a good look and then catch up with my family.

There wasn't a trail—just waist-high grass and shrubs. The ground was muddier, too. I was running now, desperate to get a look. Peering over my shoulders, I saw my family still hadn't noticed. I needed to hurry. Approaching the waterfall, I saw something come into form. It was a large blob of brown. The blob moved. Definitely a grizzly bear. He was far away, but I needed to go back.

As I was about to turn my head, I caught sight of something else. It was dark-shaped and hanging just over the edge of the waterfall. This didn't make sense. I stumbled closer to see.

It was a person. A human. Was this person hiding from the grizzly bear? Or worse, dangling from the edge, about to drop to a certain death?

"Mom! Dad!" I shouted.

They were getting out of sight. I had to run back in their direction and call again.

"Mom! Dad! Come quick!" I screamed.

The rain was picking up again, but I could see them coming. Running, in fact. I think I scared them.

"Joey!" yelled Mom. "Are you hurt?"

"Mom!" I shouted as the entire family approached. "Someone is in trouble. Look!"

They all looked. One by one, I could see light bulbs turning on in their eyes. This time, they were seeing what I saw.

"That's a grizzly!" affirmed Dad.

"Guarding a person hanging from a cliff by a waterfall!" finished Mom.

"Oh man," said Dad. He turned to face me, his stubbly face in shock. "It's been a long time since I saw someone die in real time."

CHAPTER SIXTEEN

LIFE AND DEATH

"How do we get up there?" I asked.

Dad scanned before pointing. "See to the right, at the base of the falls? That's either a human or game trail."

"Game as in grizzly?" said Mom. "You guys go ahead; I'll stay here with the younger ones."

"You know what? I don't like that." Dad's face was determined. "There's safety in numbers here. Plus, what if that bear bolts down here? I'd rather you come. Don't worry. The boys and I will fight like mad if anything happens. You're safer with us either way."

We made our way to the trail. Whatever the trail was, it was adequate, so we took some 550 paracord from our packs and started climbing. It was more like a scramble than a hike, taking us over jagged rocks, all the while watching to avoid an unhappy slip. About halfway up, the trail offered a clear view of the falls.

"Oh my goodness!" I shouted in shock. "It's Scott! Scott Melfort is trapped up there. Right beside the top edge of the waterfall!"

"He's got one foot on a small ledge," my mom cried in despair. "His other foot is just dangling. Oh my goodness. The poor boy!"

"I think he's holding onto some roots or something," said Josh. "But they don't look very big."

"And the bear's still there!" I shouted. "He's above. Close by. It's like he's eating something."

"Scott's parents, I'll bet!" cried Ellie.

"Everybody, stay behind me," commanded Dad. "Boys, we'll get some big clubs or broken tree branches for weapons. Whatever happens, do as I say!"

"Marc!" said Mom, crying some more. "You're not going to fight him! Are you crazy?"

"Honey, I've learned my lesson," said Dad. Then he did something unexpected, completely out of character, and unbelievably awesome. That is, he pulled a can of bear spray out of his jacket pocket.

I was in amazement. Mom was confused. "Lesson from what?"

We still had yet to tell her about that previous bear encounter. There was no time for that, anyway; we raced up the trail and popped our heads into the opening. Ahead of us was a sight. There was a stream gently flowing to the edge. The place was rocky, but it was still possible to move around. And the bear was in front of us, a stone's throw away.

Mr. Bear was busy tearing apart a backpack. Judging by the nylon pieces mixed with ripped and emptied food packs, it looked like he'd already shredded another pack. Thankfully, I didn't see any pieces of human flesh amidst the bear's meal.

"We need to get over to rescue Scott," said Dad. "Uh...how do we get rid of that bear? Playing dead isn't going to do anything."

"He won't move!" hissed a voice. It wasn't one of our voices, either.

Looking up, we saw a sight. Two figures were high up a lush spruce tree. It was none other than Mr. and Mrs. Melfort.

"Holy...cow!" said Dad. "What is going on?"

"The bear is a maniac!" babbled Mrs. Melfort. "He nearly swiped Bruno's head right off!"

"The old thing's too lazy to climb a tree," added Mr. Melfort. "Or maybe too big."

"But your son is hanging on the edge!" I shouted. "And you're sitting up a tree?"

They looked sheepish, as they should. What a despicable sight it was! Dad broke the silence by taking a perfect and necessary shot at Mr. Melfort.

"Easy, Joey. They don't have what we have—a large family. You see? Sometimes, it's a good thing to have a lot of people about. It helps with bears."

He scanned the scene. It didn't look promising. A bear going crazy on the remnants of that last backpack. Who knows what he'd do when he was done? The bear didn't look like he was in a defensive position. He was on offense, looking for food and destruction, come what may.

"You gonna help?" asked Dad to the Melforts. They didn't budge. Dad sighed. "Boys! You stand behind me with your sticks ready. Knives out, too. I'll lead with the spray. We'll start with light noise. But if we need to start yelling, do as I do!"

Dad stepped out of the woods and onto the rocks; he slowly inched his way forward, trying not to make direct eye contact with the bear. Josh, Johnny, and I followed behind. It seems an obvious thing to say, but I was shaking from head to toe.

"Hey bear," Dad said soothingly. "Hey bear! Time to go now."

The bear popped its head up and grunted aggressively. It didn't like being pushed out of its place.

"Hey bear," coaxed Dad once more. This time, the bear showed his disapproval. He turned to face us and growled. Then he took to heart-pounding bluff charges forward. I jumped back, but Dad held his ground. The bear paused, returned to the bag, took a swipe, and looked back at us. It was a dizzying dance of dominance.

"Bear! Back!" said Dad.

He said this just as the bear gave another bluff charge our way. This time, the beast came closer, stopping just twenty steps from where we were. He let out a piercing roar, which scared the life out of me.

"Hey! Bear!" shouted Dad. "Boys!"

We all started shouting as loud as we could. The bear spooked and ran back but went no farther than the bag. He was still in our way and unwilling to move.

We heard a pitiful cry. "Help! I'm slipping! Help!"

We couldn't see him, but we knew it was the voice of Scott coming from below the waterfall's edge.

"Boys!" said Dad. "I'm going to need to do something. I can't guarantee it will work. Our best bet is to raise heck. Be hellacious!"

With that, Dad gave another yell. We whooped as well. Dad took three steps forward. The bear growled back. His demon eyes glared now. He was an offensive bear. A hate-filled bear. I doubt this was his first encounter with humans. I had the impression he was used to victory as well.

The bear charged. Right at Dad! With precious little time to spare, Dad let his bear spray fly. At first it hit the bear in the feet, and he kept charging. Dad aimed a little higher, right to the bear's eyes.

The beast wailed in agony, but its momentum continued forward. Right towards Dad!

"Back, boys!" shouted Dad as he dodged out of the way, still spraying as the bear flew by, unable to see.

On its way past, Dad swung a stick with his left hand. We boys gave swipes with ours. Mine was feeble. In fairness, I'm only eleven!

"Ahhh!" shouted Dad. Us boys joined in.

Now the bear spray was spent, what would happen next would be life or death. The bear turned back to us but was unable to focus or see. Dad took it as an opportunity to finish what he'd started.

He took a two-handed swipe at the bear's nose with his large stick while yelling. Josh and Johnny did the same. I, too, gave my best poke.

The bear rolled back. He didn't like the screams. He really didn't like the whacks to the nose. And the spray made him downright uncomfortable. With a grunt, he took off, past the shredded backpacks, and trounced deep into the forest on the other side. He was gone.

Before I could even gasp, Dad was already racing towards the falls.

"Scott!" he shouted. "We're coming for you! Hang on!"

"Dad?" came a feeble voice. "Dad, I'm slipping!"

"It's Mr. Storthoaks. Your dad's coming too. We're going to get you. Follow me, boys. Be careful now."

I looked over at Mr. Melfort. He was still up the tree. Being on the large side of things, he was literally stuck. What a hero.

I followed my dad to the edge of the stream. Johnny, Josh, and Ellie came as well. We took a quick look. The stream was about eight feet wide and flowing almost a foot deep due to the rain. It wasn't roaring by any means, but it wasn't a peaceful few water droplets either. There was enough power to knock someone off their feet and take them over the edge if they slipped.

"I can't hold much longer!" cried Scott. "Help!"

We couldn't get down to where Scott was hanging; it was on the far side of the stream where a rock wall prevented any chance of lowering oneself. The only way to get to Scott was through the stream. The same one that shot off down the cliff.

"Boys! You'll need to lower me down the stream so I can grab Scott." Dad was trying to be brave, but his plan had several holes.

"You'll never do it!" shouted Mr. Melfort from the tree. He was stuck vertically and appeared to have a foot wedged by a tree branch. "If you slip you'll go over the edge. No one could pull you back. Too much weight!" He probably knew a thing or two about that.

"I'll do it, Dad!" I stated. I didn't even feel scared as I said it. I felt nothing except the need to help.

"Your boy can't do it either!" called Melfort from the tree. "It's no use!" His wife started bawling as he spoke.

"You're wrong about something!" Dad shouted back. "A large family has more uses than you'll ever know."

Turning to face us kids, he spoke seriously. "Joey is the lightest. He's also strong enough to do what we need. Joey, we're going to tie the paracord around your waist. It's thin, but it won't fail. Don't worry about that. We'll loop a loose end of the cord for you to have ready. You'll let Scott grab hold of that loop. Then we'll haul you up."

"The water will throw me over the edge, and I'll be dangling!" I said, now realizing the desperation of the plan.

"Not if we're a human chain!"

With that, Dad started tying knots and loops. It's amazing how old people know how to do every skill. Dad brought all the knots and lines into one big chain and tied it securely around the nearest sizeable aspen tree. When it was all done, we had a system in place. All the kids were connected to the tree, and I stepped into the water. It pushed me down but didn't take me away.

"Grab his hand!" said Dad to Ellie. She put a death grip on my arm as I carefully moved forward to the edge.

"Now! Josh, take Ellie's hand," said Dad. "Take three steps in."

Our human chain surprised me with how stable I felt. I slowly took steps forward. By now, I was only two steps from the edge.

"Johnny, you and I will hold Josh," said Dad. "Joey! Start reaching down to the edge. Don't worry, we've got you!"

I walked right to the edge. The water was roaring past me. I didn't want to look down, but I had no choice. Below me was a plunge from which nightmares are made. I was high. The bottom was low. I nearly slipped on that last rock as I took a peek over the edge. I saw a dirty-brown head of hair. I looked a little further. Two eyes were staring up at me. They were tear-stained, covered in mud, and frantic. Scott's face was white. He had vomit on his chin.

I lowered the looped end of the rope down. "Can you grab it?" I shouted.

"No!" he cried. "I can't move. I'm too stiff!"

"Scott!" I called. "You can do it! Just tell me where to lower it, then take a stab at it."

He hesitated. Debating in his mind what was possible and what was simply false hope. Finally, he called back to me. "I need it a foot lower. A little out from the water, too."

I let out more line. But to get it further from the edge was not easy. I stretched my arm as far as I could, dangling my body out so I could see perfectly downward. I saw Scott move his arm from the rock to the rope. In one jutting motion he snagged the rope. He'd done it. None too soon, either.

His foot began slipping. "Ahh!" he cried.

"Hold the rope!" I screamed. "Just hold it." With that, I shouted back, "Start pulling us back! Just a foot."

I felt the tug on the rope as well as my left arm. The rope I had dangled to Scott became taut. There was real weight behind it. We were trying to pull a human person upward through a waterfall.

"It hurts!" Scott cried.

"Falling will hurt more!" I threw back. "Use your legs to help!"

With that, I felt a surge of weight come to me. Scott must've found a place to step up with.

"Back another foot!" I shouted, instantly feeling a tug back from the water. As this happened, I saw a hand clutching the cord, shaking from strain, just in view.

"It hurts!" screamed Scott. "I'm losing it."

"Let me forward a bit!" I cried.

At that instant I lunged for Scott's hand, just as it was slipping away. I grabbed hold of two fingers.

"Ahh!" he bellowed in pain.

I couldn't do it anymore. I was losing steam. Scott was slipping away. And there was nothing in my power to stop him.

Time stopped. My heart nearly stopped, too. I was on the waterfall's edge, grasping the fingers of my greatest enemy, fighting to keep him, and myself, alive. I felt numb. Defeated. Hopeless.

My eyes lifted briefly to the mountains. A hopeless hope, a wordless prayer. Where would my help come from when I needed it the most? My need. His need. Our need.

Need. To need. To be needed. Suddenly, I thought of another time that word came into play. *"You will be needed..."*

Now was the time. I took a deep breath and acted. I adjusted my grip carefully, getting a third finger in my grasp. With razor focus, I made one quick swoop with my hand, yanking Scott's fingers forward, letting go completely, and reaching back down after them.

"Whoa!" Scott shouted in alarm.

I caught hold of him. The switch of grip worked. I now had Scott's full hand and wrist in my hand.

"Pull us back now!" I called. "Nice and slow."

The pulling came fierce. I had a death grip on Scott. That is, if I let go, it would be death.

I stepped back with the pulling. The water was still surging against my legs. Scott's head popped up from the edge. He looked half dead. Maybe he was dead?

"More!" I shouted. Unnecessary words. Everyone knew what to do.

They pulled me. I pulled Scott. Ten seconds later, his entire body emerged upwards from the edge, getting slapped with water. We had done it! He was safe!

We pulled Scott completely out of the stream and safely onto the rocks. He was shaking and white.

"Scott, you good?" called his useless Dad from the tree.

"Joey! Well done," said Dad proudly. He then looked back at Mr. Melfort. "Let's get this paracord untied. I might need it to lasso that man out of the tree."

"Yank him out hard," I said.

Shaking my head, I looked up to the mountains again. I was in need and had been needed. When I needed stability the most, my foot had not slipped. In my heart, I whispered another wordless prayer—that of thanksgiving. And I meant it.

Chapter Seventeen

Winners and Losers

How do I describe what happened next? Confusing? Upsetting? Hellacious?

We got the Melforts out of the tree. It was almost harder than rescuing Scott. At least Scott was thankful.

When we were all safe, Dad asked what happened. Scott did most of the talking. He said his family rented horses and took the proper trail to the red chairs. They were the first family to figure it out, he bragged. I mentioned something about Tom Wilson, but he kept talking like it meant nothing to him.

The family came by horseback. Just a one-day, in-and-out journey. They stopped at this stream to water the horses when the bear came. There was no bear spray, as Mr. Melfort had repeatedly bragged: "Horses outrun bears." Their horses spooked at the sight of the bear and ran. As the bear crashed towards the Melforts, the family fled in different directions. The parents ran to the tree and climbed up—no one knew how that was possible—while Scott splashed the other way across the stream. The bear took a run at Scott, and he slipped. The water carried him to the edge and over. But he was close enough to the other side of the water to grab onto a ledge as he went. It all happened so quickly.

With that, it was time to sort out a plan.

"Scott's going to freeze to death," said my dad. "Our packs are below. We'll help you down and then get a bonfire going. The boys know how to light a fire in the rain."

"That would be lovely," said Mrs. Melfort. It was the first sign of gratitude she'd given the entire ordeal. I think it was because it related to her own comfort.

At that moment, we heard rumbling in the bush.

"The bear's back!" I shouted, jumping to my feet. A brown blob was at the forest's edge.

"Settle down," said Dad. "It looks like one of their little buddies has returned."

Dad stood up and started speaking soothingly. Out of the bush stepped a strong brown horse. Dad's voice kept calling him, and the horse came. It's true, old people like Dad know how to do everything.

"Well-trained fellow," said Dad approvingly. He petted the horse's forehead gently. "Where are your buddies?"

Dad called, and sure enough, his "buddies" trotted out. Two more horses. One a little smaller for Scott. They had their saddles and bridles in place. Dad's calm voice settled them right down.

"Looks like your rides are here," I said, smiling at the gentle, powerful beasts.

"Ah, thank goodness!" said Mr. Melfort.

"We'll climb down our path," said Dad. "At the bottom we'll have that roaring fire. We might be able to make some coffee and hot chocolate too."

"Sounds great!" said Scott.

"There's another path down," said Mr. Melfort. "That's the one we were going to take. It's supposed to be good for horses. We'll use it to get down. Meet you there."

We all turned to head down. Mom and the kids started asking us a million questions.

"Was the water wet?" asked Sam. "Was it...splashy?"

"Does it taste like water?" asked Rebecca.

"Do you realize you saved someone's life?" asked Mom.

This question made me pause. Did I? I guess I was needed after all. I smiled. It wasn't so much about being a hero. I didn't do anything out of the ordinary; at least, I don't think I did. It was more about fulfilling Father Wally's kind words about me. That I had proven myself—proven his faith in me—to be true. That is why I smiled.

We got to the bottom where we'd left our packs and started making a fire. The rain had stopped. The sun was out. We got the job done. There were still no Melforts, though. So, we waited. And waited. And waited some more.

Finally, I spoke the sinking feeling I had. "You think..."

"The bear got them again?" said Rebecca.

"No. What? No! I mean, do you think they...left us in the dust and raced to the red chairs?"

"Impossible!" said Mom. "We saved their lives!"

I looked at Dad. His eyes were the size of the moon. He raced out of our treed area to the main path and looked out. Then I faintly heard some words I can't repeat here. He came back. His eyes were blazing.

"Three horses are grazing over by that structure at Moose Lake! Those"—he looked at us kids before choosing his words—"those *nimrods* double-crossed us!"

Dad stomped out the fire. We raced to get our packs sorted. Within a minute, we were jogging to Moose Lake.

"Dad, I have to go potty!" said Sam.

"Hold it!" shouted Dad. "Let's go, guys! Faster!"

We huffed and puffed our way towards the building. It was a large temporary white canvas tent with two red chairs next to it. There were people, probably workers, milling about. Moose Lake itself was a beautiful place with... Ahh, who cares!

"Faster!" shouted Dad.

With one last surge, we made it. We ran right up to the canvas tent. The tent must've had a back room because we didn't see the Melforts anywhere—just their horses.

"Welcome!" said a worker. "Congratulations!" It was a guy we'd never seen before. He called to the back of the tent, "Kelly, *they're* here! I thought they were heading to Jasper?"

Kelly popped her head out. At first she looked surprised, and even cursed once, but then she smiled sweetly. This put us off. She walked over to where we were standing and said, "Go ahead, get your picture with the chairs. Then, show us all the pictures of your adventure." Her smooth talking sounded like a witch trying to coax kids to come inside for some candy.

We did just that. We took our picture, whipped out all the pictures from our journey, and showed them to Kelly. A slight murmur from the sky could be heard as Kelly started talking.

"Well, congratulations, Storthoaks family! Wow, I never thought such a large family could do such amazing things! Do you know what place you finished? No? Well, the Storthoaks family finished..."

The murmur from the sky became louder. But we held our eyes on Kelly.

"Finished what?" I said.

"Quiet!" shouted Josh.

"You be quiet!" I said.

"All of you be quiet!" yelled Dad.

"Second place!" said Kelly.

Mom cheered. I groaned. Dad and my siblings groaned, too. The Melforts had double-crossed us. Right after we'd saved their lives.

"Do you want to know your reward?" said Kelly. Her attempts to sound soothing were like the soft hum of a buzz saw as it comes straight towards you, looking to cut and grind flesh and bone.

"Yes, please," I said.

"Your reward is..."

The sky was roaring now. Fierce wind was knocking everything around. I looked up and saw a helicopter.

"Your reward is you are all under arrest."

The helicopter touched down. It was a police chopper.

Chapter Eighteen

Banff Jail

I am here. In the present. In the Banff jail. We helicoptered here. I don't know what's happened to our vehicle. Towed away, most likely.

You've heard my story. The great Family Red Chair Challenge. The highs and lows. How I learned to build a bridge and get over myself. To need and be needed. I think it was good, even if we didn't win. It brought us together. Showed us what we were capable of. And we even saved someone's life.

Who am I kidding? I'm miserable. I'm in jail. Lyda is crying again. Mom is crying, too. I feel like crying. It's humiliating. What if Father Wally finds out? What if my friends find out—if I had friends?

I hear footsteps. Dad is perking up. Lyda's not crying anymore. Here they come. Some officers. Some National Park staff members. Kelly. And is that the Melforts? The entire family?

"Mr. and Mrs. Storthoaks..." says one of the officers. He looks like a wannabe big shot with a large mustache and slick black hair. "You have declined your right to a lawyer. You are being held on some serious charges. Do you understand?"

"No, I don't!" says Dad. He's defiant. Good!

"Let me tell you everything," says the officer, reading from a paper on his clipboard. "We have discovered that you lied about how many people were in the campsite every night. The maximum is SIX PEOPLE! You had nine!"

"I did that at a hotel, too," says Dad, rolling his eyes. "If you want to add a few more years to our prison time."

"Don't roll your eyes!" says the officer. "Of course, your most serious charge is assault and attempted murder."

"What?" says Mom.

"You nearly killed me at Lake O'Hara!" says Mr. Melfort, his face turning ugly. Uglier, I should say.

"I was drowning, for heaven's sake!" shouts Dad.

"Did you not learn to never stand in—to not—a canoe stand—never?" I say. I'm getting flustered. Can you tell?

"Quiet!" says the officer, glaring at us. "That is no way to treat an honest family man. A tireless, successful business-man. A respected member of the government. An honor-able cabinet minister to the prime minister."

"What?" says Josh. "This McButterpants?"

"Hey!" snarls Mr. Melfort, Bigshot Extraordinaire.

"I'll add that to your charge," says the officer, writing down on the paper. "A hate crime! Also! In addition! And more! Henceforth! You uttered threats to said honorable person. On multiple occasions. You evaded the law. Parked illegally. Injured protected wildlife—in this case, a poor, defenseless grizzly bear—and camped at a backcountry lo-cation without a proper permit."

"And," interrupts Mr. Melfort, getting too big for his massive britches, "you broke the law, too!"

The officer finishes his writing and hands the clipboard to Mr. Melfort. "Sign right here, Mr. Melfort," says the officer. "This will make it all official."

I look at Mr. Melfort. He's grinning from ear to ear, like a spoiled kid on Christmas Day. He signs the paper and then whips it in front of our faces to show us—to gloat like an immature...nimrod. I see a scribbled *Bruno MelFort*. This makes me pause for a second.

"We want a lawyer now!" I say.

"Too late!" says Mr. MelFort. I swear he stuck out his tongue after.

"Er, um," stammers the officer. "Why, of course. Who should I call?"

"Uh... We want the best defense in town," says Dad.

"We want Harlan Foxman!" I shout.

"No!" screams Kelly.

Dad gives me a look. He then smiles. "Yes, we want Harlan Foxman."

"But he's not a lawyer," stammers Kelly.

"I know," I say. "He's just an ordinary guy."

We have to wait only five minutes. Harlan Foxman is just down the street. Probably helping old ladies cross the road. What a good guy.

"It's the Storthoaks family!" says Harlan as he walks in. His kind eyes glow with warmth and care. Then they frown. "Wait! Holy moly! You're in the slammer!"

"Harlan," says Dad, "we're being charged with everything under the sun. We're wondering how the investigation *actually* went down."

"That's enough!" interrupts Kelly.

"Lock 'em away!" shouts Mr. MelFort.

"Throw away the key!" adds his wife.

"We *are* locked away, you hellacious nimrod," I say. These are my new favorite words. Mom shrieks. Dad laughs.

Harlan looks down and shuffles his feet. He's uncomfortable. He's unsure of what to say. I look at him—this ordinary guy. I realize at that moment that the best people are ordinary. They have the determination to do what is right, even if it is hard. I believe in Harlan.

"Harlan, do you ever wish you were a policeman?" I ask.

"Heck no!" he says, almost spitting in surprise. The officer beside him grunts his disapproval.

"I think I'd like to be one," I say. I can see the officer perk up. "You have to be strong and brave." Now he's sticking out his chest.

"Sure," says Harlan. "I suppose."

"Did you know Tom Wilson was once a policeman?"

"Oh really?" says Harlan, smiling. "That's interesting."

"This kid's wasting our time!" interrupts Mr. MelFort. "We don't have time to hear about Tom Whoever."

"You don't like Tom Wilson?" I ask.

"Never heard of him. Hope he's dead for all I care," says Mr. MelFort.

A hush settles over the room. Now, it is Kelly who starts shuffling her feet uncomfortably.

I look at Dad; he nods his head. Maybe he's figured out where I'm going with all this.

"Harlan, what company has been setting up all these awesome rides and attractions for the Family Red Chair Challenge?" I ask.

"Why, BMF, of course."

"Stop wasting our time!" yells Mr. MelFort. I notice his son Scott nearby. Scott is looking sad. Guilty even.

"Harlan," I keep at it, "How much of the Family Red Chair Challenge money has stayed in the parks?"

"Not a penny!" shouts Harlan.

Now Mr. MelFort is in a rage. I'm scared of him. Thankfully, I'm behind bars. It's my safe space. I take one last swipe.

"Harlan, could you please look up who owns BMF?"

"I sure will!" beams Harlan.

Before Harlan can add any other words, Mr. MelFort charges at me. There are bars in the way. But he still tries to swipe at my face with his hand, like a grizzly bear with five bullet wounds.

"Dad!" shouts Scott.

"Mr. MelFort!" says the officer. "That's enough!"

"Officer," I say, "Mr. MelFort owns the company. I know it. Bruno MelFort. BMF. He's the one making the money. Look it up, Harlan! And Mr. MelFort also cheated to win! He doesn't know the code. He doesn't know who Tom Wilson is nor about the snowshoe story when he lost his toes. MelFort's a cheater! A fraud! And *she's* the one who helped him!"

I point at Kelly. She tries to run, but Harlan gets in her way. She then turns to me and glares. I know it is over. Suddenly, a little voice booms large.

"Dad!" says Scott. "The Storthoaks family saved my life!"

"They did?" asks the officer.

"They sure did!" Scott then tells them the story at the waterfall with the bear. Harlan smiles as he hears it. He's proud. This makes me proud.

When Scott is finished, the officer turns to me and says, "Well done, son. Well done! We might have the wrong people in jail right now."

"And I know we have the wrong people as winners of the Family Red Chair Challenge," says Harlan. He smiles. I smile. Scott smiles. Everyone smiles. Except for Kelly and Mr. MelFort.

All is well.

CHAPTER NINETEEN

THERE AND BACK AGAIN

"Joey!" shouts Dad. "Did you check for cats this time?"

"Yep," I say. "It's a guarantee. Or your money back."

We are on our way to church. *Our* church. In *our* town of Saskariver. We are home now. There and back again, a misfit's journey.

I am a changed person, I think. For one, I have a new ball glove and bat. That's basically a new me. In fact, everyone in our family got something new. Dad says we earned it. We earned the $25,000. Mom says we should save the money for our future education. I know what she's saying. But if education is important, baseball is importanter.

The Mass begins. I take Sam out to the washroom at the appointed time. After, we step outside into the morning sun. It beats warm and free. I am free.

Free from jail, yes. That came easy enough. For us, anyway. Dad says Mr. MelFort might not have such an easy time of things. Legal stuff. Scandal, even. I don't want to sound mean, but that's his problem. You do the crime, you do the time. I feel bad for Scott, though. He deserves better. I'm thinking of writing to him. I hope to keep in touch. Who knows? Maybe life will be easier for him now. Or at least happier.

I hope to return to the mountains someday. To see them as they are meant to be. Harlan Foxman says he's confident the national parks will become normal again. Unspoiled from gimmicks and noise. They will be free. I'd love to see this. To see the towering peaks, with maybe a shadow of a cloud blocking a timeless glacier, joining heaven to earth. To smell the wildflowers high in the subalpine meadows, fresh and life-giving. To feel gentle streams pass between my toes, cold and healing. To dip my hands in these streams and cup a mouthful of water. Straight from the glacier, crisp and untamed. To hear the echoes of trains passing through spirals in the night. To listen to the haunting sound of an owl under the stars. To understand a higher power watches over us.

I think of Tom Wilson and his larger-than-life adventures. Mary Schaffer and her dedication. Philip Stanley Abbot and his fall from the heights. Of Wild Bill Peyto, Jim Brewster, James Hector, and many more. They all seem so extraordinary. But maybe they weren't? Maybe they felt pain and needs like everyone else but had just a little more determination. I think of Harlan Foxman. There are still legends walking among us.

A cat meows next to our van. My guarantee fails. It's from a new batch of kittens. The little thing is nameless. I look at Sam. He grins and points to the window where the choir is singing. I shake my head. Not today. Maybe not ever again. The cat will have to sit outside and wait. I return inside the church and even listen to some of the preaching.

It's after Mass now. I talk with Father Wally. I start telling him of my adventure. He smiles patiently. I can tell he's pleased.

"And then, after we got out of jail, Dad drove us home using the David Thompson highway! Did you know that David Thompson once hurt his leg on..."

I pause. I'm getting carried away again.

"Yes, Joey. I read the book before I gave it to you." Father winks as he says this.

Dad calls for me to get in the vehicle. He's holding the kitten. I mutter one last question to Father Wally before I leave.

"Thanks for the book! And the message. There's just one thing I don't get. Psalm 12-1? It makes no sense! Something about no one being loyal anymore..."

"Oh, mamma mia!" says Father Wally. "I must've scribbled it wrong! No, I meant to write Psalm *121*! Mamma mia!"

I go to the vehicle, and we drive home. I tell my family that we should name this new kitten Harlan. They agree. Harlan looks at me. His short gray fur is relaxed, his green eyes adventurous and trusting.

At home, my parents start cooking pancakes. Dozens and dozens of pancakes. All food tastes amazing now after weeks of peanut butter and jelly wraps. I sneak by them to find our Bible in the living room. I am stealthy. An eleven-year-old can't let people see him reading the Bible. They might expect me to behave all the time. I'm not ready for that quite yet.

I find what I am looking for. Psalms 121. I start reading.

I lift up my eyes to the mountains—where does my help come from? My help comes from the LORD, the Maker of heaven and earth. He will not let your foot slip...

I stop there. It is enough. I smile. The prophecy is fulfilled.

I close the Good Book and look out the window. I don't see mountains—just trees and fields. My Rocky Mountain challenge is over. It is time to return to my ordinary life. My simple life. My life where ordinary mingled with determination can set a world afire. Even for a misfit. I smile. The world *needs* no less.

And from the kitchen, I hear a yell.

"Joey! Harlan's inside the house! And he just left a puddle on the kitchen floor!"

Ordinary, but never dull.

THE END

LEAVE A PAWSITIVE
AMAZON REVIEW!

ACKNOWLEDGMENTS

My wife: I guess that English degree you got is getting put to good use after all... Thanks for being the greatest, most beautiful, and best-ever beta reader. And thanks for getting that M.R.S. degree too!

My children: For being such willing and energetic outdoor adventurers. Anything is possible! Like eating rehydrated food for days and days on end.

The staff at the Whyte Museum: Your place gave me the true feel of those early pioneers. And your digital archives continue to be a real treasure.

My editor, the amazing Shavonne Clarke: Believe it or not, as a child I never intended on becoming a writer! (Shavonne, I'm sure you believe it quite readily.)

Edward Cavell, John Whyte (RIP), and Faye Reineberg Holt: Your books (*Rocky Mountain Madness, Canada's Rocky Mountains*) provided many valuable insights, images, and laughs.

My launch team: If I were you, I'd have banned emails from *Daniel J. Millette* years ago. Yet you still stick with me through it all. I cannot thank you enough.

Harlan Fox and Marty Up North: I couldn't quite get to every mentioned hike in this book. Your YouTube channels, with all their footage and insight, more than satisfied for what was lacking on my part.

All the students I've ever taught: For bouncing so many ideas off you, and receiving such appreciated feedback. You're like little guinea pigs to me! But seriously, thanks for the inspiration, enthusiasm, and assistance.

The Good Lord: *I lift up my eyes to the mountains—where does my help come from? My help comes from the LORD, the Maker of heaven and earth.* All glory to God.

A Mission for All

"You groovy?" asked the man. I'd say he was a hippy if I didn't know any better—an honest-to-goodness hippy.

"I'm good," I lied.

"Forest," said an old lady in a hemp hat, long white dress, and rainbow necklace, "I think he's got Amazon problems."

The man, apparently named Forest, nodded. "Don't we all, Chick."

"I'm just frustrated," I said. Of all the people to open up to...an old hippy couple! "I have this story out about my Rocky Mountain adventures. It's pretty epic. People love it. But then Amazon just won't push it for others to see. I don't get it."

"Just like the Bezos, man," said Forest. "Gotta crush the little dude from his yacht."

"Something like that," I said before adding a "dude."

"You know, young story-book character man, life is like a book review," said Chick. "It's not about the book with Amazon. It's the review that lets us all fly. Like, you get book reviews, good ones, and they give the little guy a break."

I didn't know what she was saying.

"There's a saying I really dig," interrupted Forest. "Write a book and you'll feed a man for a day. Get a bunch of book reviews on Amazon, and you'll feed a man for a lifetime. Far out, hey?"

"You mean Amazon will show others my book if I just get more book reviews?" I asked.

"You can do whatever your hip heart sets itself on," said Chick, "as long as you have those reviews!"

"Uh, I need to go tell people. The readers, I mean," I said.

"Look, son," said Forest. "Chill. We just left a review. A psychedelic one. And I'll just tell these groovy readers right now to do the same."

"Wow, thanks!" I said.

"Hey readers out there," said Forest. "Defy the government, man. Go fly, little doves, to your device and give this young Joey a good Amazon review. Copacetic?"

HEADING TO THE ROCKY MOUNTAINS?

When I first started writing this book a news story broke of two people dying from exposure while hiking in the Rocky Mountains. As I write this last section, another news story has come of a couple (and their dog) killed by a grizzly bear in Banff National Park. Both occurrences are extremely rare but still possible.

Whatever interest you may have in hiking and exploring the great outdoors, *always* follow sound advice, do your research, and make proper preparations, be it with attire, bear spray, or developing survival skills. Your life matters too much to take foolish risks. What I mean to say is, I assume no responsibility for anything that may happen to you!

With this necessary warning aside, let's talk hiking! My family loves it so much we spend the winter months dreaming of our next mountain adventure. You can check out some of our trips at: https://www.youtube.com/@DanielJMillette/videos

I will throw out some advice, favorites, and random tidbits. Read, or ignore, as you please.

-Our favorite campground is Kicking Horse Campground in Yoho National Park. You have to be okay with hearing the faint echoes of trains winding through the nearby spiral tunnels in the night. Book a campsite early.

-Our five favorite family hikes of all time:

1) Mt. Edith Cavell (Jasper)
2) Yoho Lake/Iceline Ridge (Yoho)
3) Helen Lake (Banff)
4) Stanley Glacier (Kootenay)
5) Bow Glacier Falls (Banff)

-Personally, I would never hike with a dog. Dogs and bears get along as well as the Storthoaks and Melfort families do.

-Speaking of bears, we frequently see people hiking with a small bear bell to make warning noises. I find that hiking with five noisy children works much better.

-We also see families hike with the dad carrying a massive backpack of supplies while his children (often teenagers) have no loads to haul. Wrong! Children can carry packs too. Our one son has so much energy he actually *needs* a pack to weigh him down a bit.

-Dehydrating your food beforehand is a game-changer when camping. No more stops at grocery stores! And the food is every little bit as good as if it were fresh. Even better, in fact, because you're eating it while staring at mountains.

-The best starter hikes, I think, are either Old Fort Point (Jasper), Emerald Lake Loop (Yoho), or Tunnel Mountain (Banff... Leave early to beat the crowds).

-Hiking boots are worth the expense. Trekking poles too.

-If you love crowds and excitement, go to Banff. Otherwise, camp and hike elsewhere. As you might've guessed from this book, we're partial to quiet places away from people.

-For said peace and quiet, visit busy locations in the evening. Most people will have left. We have beautiful memories of strolling around Takakkaw Falls (Yoho) or Annette Lake (Jasper) at sunset, all alone. Even Lake Louise only has about five thousand people on its shores in the evening...and they don't charge for parking after 7:00 p.m.

-Our best trips have always been where we plan meticulously. Just showing up and seeing what's out there can be iffy.

-All of this is to say, I hope you get out and enjoy exploring the outdoors!

Bonus!

Y ou will not want to miss other books in the
Adventures of a Misfit series!
I present to you an excerpt from *My Blasted Town*.

I'm half sure I'm dead right now. At *least* half sure. Only two things keep me from 100% certainty. First, I've got a sharp pain in my left arm from the fall. I'd thought, or hoped, that death would remove all pain. That there would be no sting. But no dead person ever warned me what to expect. And second, I haven't seen Jesus anywhere. Not yet. Maybe Jesus is taking his time getting to me. How long should I wait?

No, I must be dead. At first, there were stars in my mind when I fell. Like sparks of electricity piercing an endless night. Now, there is just this endless night. All darkness. My world has collapsed. I am already in the grave. It is cold, hard, and creepy. Not a pleasant way to go. The Egyptians had the right idea by burying their dead with all their stuff.

I could use my dog Doggy right now. I would even be sort of happy with one of my cats.

Did I mention it is dark? Dark, lonely, and getting colder. Rest in peace, Joey Storthoaks. At the ripe old age of eleven. Only the sort-of-good die young.

What brought me to this place? What am I doing *here*? That is my story, and seeing as Jesus might be a little late in coming to get me, I don't mind sharing it.

I must admit I've been here before. And where is that? The Saskariver Cemetery. It's near the river's edge, surrounded by evergreen forest and willow bush. Deer, moose, and bears make their way to the cemetery. Skunks, cougars, and coyotes too. It's a regular meeting place. I never feared such critters here, though. I feared much worse.

In the woods behind the Saskariver Cemetery lives a man. One might call him homeless, but that would be incorrect. He lives out in the bush behind the graves because he chooses to do so. It is his home. As with the bears, cougars, and coyotes, this man wants to be close to the graves. The constant presence of death is his comfort.

I'm told that this man buries his victims behind the cemetery—that the animals come to receive scraps of...food from him. I'm told he's always looking for his next victim, that even the police are scared of him, that he even once made a victim out of a policeman. I'm told he once lost a child in an accident and that it messed with his head. I'm told he has a patch over one eye because the covered eye is a demon's.

I'm told these things because I live in a small town in Saskatchewan, Canada. Every small town has a story like this. And it is a right of passage for every young person to investigate it. To go *there*. To live, to tell. If not to live, then to decrease the surplus population. I did just that one day. I did go *there*, with my older brother Josh and our friend Xander Humboldt. I am younger than both of them by three years. I suppose that put me in a difficult spot. The youngest must always do the dirty work. One of these days I'll make my younger brother Sam do the same. If I get back to life.

It was early May, and the leaves hadn't quite filled the trees yet. We were at church that Friday evening. There was a youth group retreat of sorts. It was either attending the youth group or cleaning the chicken coop at home. I should've stayed home and cleaned the chicken coop. Chickens don't try to lay hands on you to heal you.

Inside the church, there was some form of music to occupy our time. You know the songs where the boys sing the first part, the girls sing the second, then all join together on the final go-around? Imagine boys having to rhyme words like fire and desire while singing next to a group of girls. "You light my *fire*... My heart's *desire*..." It's meant for God, I think. But I swear some of those girls take it in other ways. They blush and glow. Some of the boys like that. Not me. Well, on that one night, the songs became giggle-fests. The youth group leaders threatened to "lay hands" over us in prayer to have us smarten up.

We smartened up just in time for the testimonial section. Teenagers were crying over how they had found Jesus. These teenagers were the same ones who swore and smoked behind the school just hours earlier. But I'm sounding bitter. I'm just jealous that I still have yet to find Jesus here in my grave.

The church retreat was getting emotional. Josh and Xander did the only sensible thing they could and snuck out into the cool spring evening. I would've left with a friend my age, but I don't have any friends worth mentioning. Friendship isn't my strong suit. So, I snuck out with Josh and Xander. We made our way to the nearby cemetery. Darkness was settling in, where just enough light was available to see what was ahead of you. A vague, shadowy vision. Like a horror movie.

"What are we doing?" I asked Xander and Josh.

"Shut up and keep quiet!" yelled Xander, unaware of the irony of his words. "You're the slowest here, aren't you? We can leave you behind alone if we want, dead or alive," he threatened. Thirty minutes earlier, Xander had been testifying at the retreat that he was a perfectly saved young man.

I followed the boys right through the graveyard. We were heading west towards the bush near the river. A tombstone reached out and tripped me. I stumbled forward, right into Josh's backside. He tumbled over onto Xander, who in turn knocked over a solar lantern resting near an old grave where the words "Rest in Peace" shouted a warning at us.

Feeling somehow responsible for my mess-up, my brother amended the situation, knocking me flat on my back and hissing, "If you get us killed, then I'll kill you!" I knew he meant it, too.

We made our way to the cemetery's edge and shimmied through branches and trees toward the last glimpses of light. The rose bushes scraped at my cheeks as we passed through, but I didn't make a sound.

"Shh, you brat!" shouted Xander, again unaware of himself. "I think I see something through the bush."

"Is that a blue tarp?" asked Josh, peering through the remaining cover of branches and trees.

My heart pounded through my chest, into my limbs, and echoed to the rest of the world. Not a blue tarp! Anything but a blue tarp.

"It's set up like a tent," added Xander. "Someone *does* live here. It's true. It's real." He turned towards us and said, "It's gonna kill us."

My brother Josh did the only thing he knew possible at that dreadful moment. With his voice shaking like the pelvis of Elvis, he offered a great sacrifice for the good of all. That is, he sacrificed his own brother.

"Joey, go check it out," he said. "We'll watch from here to see if anyone comes."

"I'm not..."

"Get going! Or else I'll tell Mom who's been sneaking the chips at night."

Checkmate. That was worse than his threat to kill me. I knew I was done. I took a step forward. The air was thick with tension. Another step. A chill ran through my bones. Two more steps. Before I knew it, I was standing in a small clearing, maybe thirty feet in diameter. There indeed was a blue tarp set up like a tent. I saw rusty cans and old bottles.

A makeshift fireplace was in the middle of it all. And a small table. It was probably an altar of sacrifice where cats and eleven-year-old children were offered.

"Hurry up!" bellowed Xander from the bush, with his usual lack of self-awareness.

Unsure of what I was supposed to do, I panicked and bent to pick up an old bottle to bring back with me. Sort of a souvenir to prove my courage. Like that hobbit did once in the dragon's lair. But it was getting dark, and as I reached to pick up what I thought was a dark wine bottle, instead, my hand clutched something soft and warm. The warm blob exploded at the touch, jumped three feet in the air, and screeched a murderous yell.

"Scram!" shouted Xander.

It was every man for himself. I jumped out of my skin, nearly out of my soul, and dove into the bush. The cat I had evidently disturbed fled in front of me. I unknowingly stepped on its tail this time as I scrambled for cover. That darn cat. We both went sprawling. My face landed on the edge of one of those rose bushes, the kind where even the tiniest of pricks makes you want to cry like a baby, and I crawled on all fours into those thorns in front of me. Just as my backside was covered and I was near passing out with a half-inch thorn in my chin, I heard a grizzly man's voice from the bush on the other side of the clearing.

"I'm coming for you!"

Off like a shot. Through the bush, through thorns and willows, and into the cemetery. Xander and Josh were already gone from sight. Possibly they were back in the church by now, claiming to be saved. Not me. I was still halfway through the cemetery. No man's land. Death literally all around. I needed saving, alright.

A crackle sounded from the trees behind me. What to do? As I ran, I saw a piece of plywood on the ground next to a mound of dirt. The plywood was covering a large hole. The hole was undoubtedly made to welcome a dead body in the next day or two. I had two choices: go in this hole, temporarily, or be caught by the creep and end up in one of his holes, permanently. It was no choice at all. I stopped at the edge of this fresh hole, breathed, and jumped in.

It's true. They do dig graves six feet down. And it's also true, a six-foot hole is deep. A-foot-over-my-brown-hair deep. What on earth was I thinking? I was trapped. Unable to shout for help for fear of attracting the local killer. Unable to move. This was my first experience of life in the grave. Not to be my last.

Also at Amazon:

ABOUT THE AUTHOR

Daniel J. Millette is a husband, father, writer, and educator living in North East Saskatchewan. Millette has a love for meaningful storytelling, as well as for mountain adventures with his family.

Please subscribe/like at YouTube, Facebook, Substack, or all three.

"The wide world is all about you: you can fence your-selves in, but you cannot for ever fence it out."

J.R.R. Tolkien, *The Fellowship of the Ring*

Manufactured by Amazon.ca
Acheson, AB

14316735R00102